Help

Mental Illness to Wellness

The Impact of Food on Our Mental Health

Carolyn Marsalis, M.Ed., CHHC
Amy Pierce, CPS

with a foreword by Tennie McCarty

Printed in the United States of America

Book cover photo by: Amy Pierce

Book editing by: Carolyn Marsalis and Christina Proper

ISBN 978-0-9976183-03

For all diagnosed with mental illness.

Disclaimer

We are not medical doctors, and we are not giving medical advice. This book is in no way intended to be used as medical advice. As with anything regarding your health, consult with your own doctor for such advice. We are simply sharing our personal journeys from mental illness to mental wellness.

About the Cover

The book cover is a photograph taken with a cell phone. The image was found on the back of a bathroom stall door in Terrell State Hospital. We chose to use this picture as it powerfully elicits a sense of complete desperation. We have both felt that desperation throughout our lives. We wrote the word "Help" many times in our journals.

Table of Contents

Foreword

Dear Reader:

These precious, smart, beautiful women suffered from addiction, depression, suicidal ideation, and eating disorders for over 20 years. Their pain took them to depths I can only imagine. As I read word after word of their stories, I cried. I *knew* these women. I was one of the many professionals along their path who tried to help them. Over and over again, I heard only of their relapse—as a clinician, I felt powerless.

I have been successfully recovering from an Eating Disorder (Binge Eating Disorder and Bulimia) for the past 30 years. About 10 years ago, I began to have stomach problems. It seemed as though anything I put in my mouth would cause my stomach to swell to the point that I looked as if I were nine months pregnant. After seeing several doctors for a diagnosis, no one had a clue what was wrong with me. As a last resort, I agreed to have exploratory surgery on my stomach. The surgery was scheduled for January 26, 2006. On my way home from the surgeon's office, I called my dear friend, Dr. Kathy Easterling, in Atlanta, Georgia. I told her the doctor advised me to have surgery. Kathy begged and pleaded with me to put off having surgery for 30 days and use that time to detox from all gluten products. For years, Kathy encouraged me to become gluten free. I always responded, "I'm not allergic to anything." Long story short, I have been gluten free and symptom free since that time—without surgery.

When I heard from Carolyn and Amy about their journeys and the dramatic changes which took place in their lives simply because they altered their daily food plan, I was amazed. They found a remarkable solution for their lifelong problems. Truly, it is by the grace of God these two women are alive. To read or hear of something you've experienced yourself is exciting. It's a validation to your own reality.

I am so grateful to God for allowing Carolyn's and Amy's paths to cross again after all these years. During Amy's stay at Shade of Hope, I observed the connection Carolyn made with Amy. In some way, it gave Amy a ray of hope. I believe in miracles, not just the ones we read about in the Bible, but present day miracles. I know beyond a shadow of a doubt, the discovery these two women have made in their journey with gluten is a miracle! I also believe God is going to use these two beautiful creatures to help others who are suffering from food intolerances and food allergies.

Carolyn and Amy, your pain has not been in vain. You have much work in front of you. Please continue on your paths—so many people need to hear your "Experience, Strength, and Hope."

Light and Love,

Tennie McCarty, LCDC, ADC III, CEDC
Founder and CEO, Shades of Hope Treatment Center
Buffalo Gap, TX

Introduction

When my dear friend, Carolyn, asked me to write an introduction for her book, I was overwhelmed. What started out to be a "chance" meeting ended up as a series of profound events that changed her life—and mine. When I first met Carolyn, she seemed like a very nice woman who was well-mannered and looked as normal as normal can be. I recall her being a bit timid as we chatted casually. As the conversation went on, she expressed a desire to make an appointment with me for nutritional help. There was something unique about her—something I instinctively liked. I wanted the opportunity to help her. Little did I know, she had all but given up hope of ever living a normal life. I can assure you that the experiences she shares on the following pages are only a very small part of what actually occurred in her life. Her story is incredibly moving and largely inconceivable.

Mental illness is a crime of the mind. It is considered a disease—a nation-wide epidemic, for which our medical establishment has no definitive answers. Psychiatry attempts to claim understanding of an individual's mind, even though the owner of that mind cannot understand or express what is happening to them. Families and friends of these individuals often have no clue about what's happening in the patient's internal world.

The medical and psychiatric systems we have in place only treat the symptoms—*not the cause*. I do not agree with the current system's approach. The only options agreed upon are to drug them up, lock them up, or both. Most treatments are a chemical cover-up, peppered with undesirable side effects. These medications and treatments—*intended to stabilize an assumed instability*—deaden one's ability to think, dull one's sense of self, and decrease the desire for getting well. Many individuals diagnosed and treated with mental illnesses are medicated into giving up. The cycles of medication, therapy, rehabilitation, isolation and limitation of social interaction repeat indefinitely. This ultimately strips individuals of their identities, robs them of their relationships, and traps them in a house of horrors which is beyond description.

People are not born with a Prozac deficiency, nor do they develop one later in life. One does not need Lithium to stabilize the mind. There is no internal deficiency of Seroquel, Adderall or Provigil, nor do we acquire such deficiencies. I am of the opinion that mental illness is a state of dysfunction which has a root cause. In the past 50 years, we have seen an exponential increase in a wide number of diseases. Along with new mental health diagnoses being added to the list every few years, the rise in autism, diabetes, irritable bowel syndrome, Hashimoto's Disease, acid reflux, depression, and other diseases is staggering.

In my practice as a traditional Naturopathic Doctor with a Ph.D. in Nutrition, hundreds and hundreds of patients have come to my office with a long list of seemingly unrelated symptoms. It is my opinion that all are rooted in diet and the health of the digestive tract. Specifically, I have found that my patients are missing microbes. We are all made of microbes—roughly 10 trillion of them. In essence, microbes rule our existence. These bacteria live both in and on our bodies and contribute more to our gene pool than anything else. Simply said, they play a leading role in immune health, mental health, emotional health, and are responsible for how well the body eliminates waste every day.

The largest concentration of bacteria, known as the microbiome, resides in the large intestine. Within this large concentration, certain bacteria play a crucial role in the way one's mind works. Those particular bacteria create important neurotransmitters and other chemical messengers that keep one stable, happy, and able to maintain a healthy mental state. When these bacteria have a healthy environment to live in, all is well. However, if the intestinal environment becomes unhealthy, these messages can become confused, disoriented and scrambled, leaving one to feel as though the body and mind are disconnected.

Certain foods can speed up the rate at which these messages become scrambled, making the situation even worse. When these foods are part of a regular diet, they can alter the intestinal microbiome dramatically, causing physical, mental and emotional changes that may not be noticed initially. One of the biggest food offenders is a certain protein complex. The negative effects of this protein are not going away anytime soon. This protein is found in our most commonly consumed grain—gluten.

Carolyn and Amy were able to radically alter the course of their lives in a profound way after removing this seemingly innocuous substance called gluten. Both have completely reversed their diagnoses of mental illness and are living fulfilling lives today. Their decision to remove this one food item from their diets allowed them freedom from the painful prisons they lived in for so many years.

In the pages that follow, listen to their pain, get inside their prisons, feel their isolation and abandonment. If you are one who struggles with any kind of mental illness or other related diagnosis, you may have just found your answer. I encourage all to take their words to heart. These two women are taking a stand for you and for everyone else who has lived with this kind of pain. When you hear how their minds and hearts became *alive* once they made this simple change, *believe it!*

Dr. Ronda L. Nelson, ND, MH, CNC
Founder and President, Restoration Health, Inc.
International Teacher and Speaker
Seattle, WA

Authors' Note

The following narratives are our best recollections of the events in our lives. They are in no way exhaustive. We will include some events—not many. While events play a huge role in our lives, it's not the events we are interested in sharing; it is the experience of living we wish to share. The sequence of events may not add up with what others recall. Our journeys and stories are very different. We walked vastly different paths, yet we come together to share our experience of stepping from illness into wellness.

While writing this book, our greatest fear was that people would read it and pity us. We ask only that you think about what it must have been like to live our lives and walk in our shoes. In the following pages, we pull back the curtains and open the windows to give you a peek inside our lives as we traveled on this journey to wellness and complete recovery. We share our stories in the hope that others may find glimpses of themselves in what we say, and possibly discover *help* in an unexpected place.

Carolyn & Amy

Part One

Carolyn

I was an underweight baby and was supposedly born with a condition called spastic stomach which meant that I threw up many of the bottles I was fed. What was supposed to be nourishment was making me throw up. My great-grandmother was one of the only people able to successfully feed me in the early days—probably because not much rattled her.

My mother said that as an infant I preferred to sit in my infant seat rather than be held. This story makes complete sense to me. My skin always hurt. I couldn't stand to be touched lightly, nor could I tolerate loose clothing. I always slept in pajamas that fit like a body suit. I hated for the fan or the heating and air-conditioner to blow on me. My great grandmother was the only one of my grandparents who let me sleep with her because she didn't mind my kicking legs. Mostly, I had to sleep on the floor when visiting, because I kicked so much.

When I was four years old, my parents were out of town and I was staying with my grandparents. I got really sick and became dehydrated because I had been vomiting so much. I was taken to the hospital where my grandfather was a doctor. I remember lying in that hospital bed; it was dark and scary there. I'm not sure I breathed the whole time I was there. Those were not the days of cheerful nursing. This was just the beginning of many doctor visits, shots, and hospitalizations.

When I was six years old, I had my tonsils taken out because I had so many sore throats and ear infections. I got glasses and my eyesight worsened every time I went to the eye doctor. I had six cavities the first time I went to the dentist; I have dental work in more teeth than not. I had bronchitis every year and/or the flu which always lasted at least a full week. I remember many times lying on the bathroom floor and being given enemas—*I hated those things.*

In elementary school, my bedtime was 7 pm because my mother had too much trouble waking me up in the mornings. It was not unusual for her to find me bent over the bottom dresser drawer asleep—I was supposed to be getting dressed for school. By this time, I had the name "sleepy head." It was nothing for me to sleep 12 hours a day. I was always tired.

Physical activity was hard for me. I was constantly struggling in Physical Education class. Every part of me felt heavy. I was tall and lean—deemed healthy by the doctor—life should have been easy. No matter how hard I tried, I couldn't make my body move well. I just wanted to be like other kids. I wanted to run fast and jump high. I always came in last when we raced or we were timed in P.E. I got sick every year at summer camp and the owner would have to take me to town 30 miles away to go see the doctor. I hated having to spend my camp time in the infirmary.

Throughout my school years, I often sobbed uncontrollably: convulsive, heaving sobs—the kind of sobbing where I couldn't catch my breath and then I'd throw up. The first time I remember it happening, I was in second grade. My teacher, reprimanded me for talking to my friend when we were supposed to be working. I started crying so hard and couldn't stop. The other kids began calling me a "cry baby." My teacher pulled me out of the room to ask why I was crying. I couldn't answer her.

In moments of panic or fear I could never get the words out of my mouth to tell anyone what was wrong. I would just stand there and shake my head back and forth saying, "I don't know," over and over. It was as if I was trapped in quicksand. I was simply unable to tell anyone what was happening. My brother got sick too, but he didn't stay sick for a week, didn't get cavities, didn't get glasses, didn't have to have enemas, wasn't skinny, didn't have thin hair, and something had to be "really wrong" for him to cry.

Along with frequent tears, I had a stomach ache almost every day after lunch. My mom would come pick me up early from school. I would cry until I was completely spent and then I would sleep. This happened many, many times. It wasn't long before my parents told me I couldn't miss school anymore unless I had a fever, which was rare. From then on, when I complained about anything physically— which had no apparent proof like a fever or bronchitis—I was ignored.

During junior high school, I had to drag myself through P.E., I had horrible menstrual cramps every month, and I cried way too easily. I was made fun of and had very few friends. I lived for the weekends where I could escape on my horse. My horse was like sweet freedom to me. Nothing could touch me when I rode. I was carried away to a place of peace and tranquility. No demands. No need for conversation—just me and my horse. I loved riding horses; that was easy—all I had to do was sit there. Riding was the one area of my life I could control. I couldn't control the tears and I couldn't control the anxiety. I could control that big animal and I was good at it.

I took ballet all through school and loved my classes, but no matter how much I practiced, I was never selected to dance in major productions. I simply couldn't get my body to do what it was supposed to do—*and* I would start crying if I made a mistake.

When I was in the 7th grade, a girl from a nearby neighborhood told me she was going to beat me up the next time I rode the bus home from school. I had never been more terrified. I didn't know what to do. I could not find the words to respond to this threat. I stood there frozen. I had seen plenty of boys get beat up in my neighborhood; they got black eyes and bloody noses. I went home and told my mother. She began driving me to and from school. I was the only kid in the neighborhood who didn't ride the bus. Everyone knew why, which brought on a lot of harassment at school.

"Cry baby" and "lazy bones" were my nicknames.

4

The names became more criticizing and disapproving as I grew older. I was frequently told to grow a "thicker skin" and quit being so sensitive. I didn't have the stamina, the energy, or the ability to deal with my life the way others seemed to deal with theirs.

2

When I was a freshman in high school, my grades were hit and miss for a smart kid, which made my daddy furious. I was accused of being lazy and not doing the work required—I reacted with sarcasm. I was either sleeping too much or being way too irritable and surly for my parent's liking. From the outside, it appeared that I didn't care about my work. I did care, but I had no answers for what was happening to me. I didn't understand what was going on, so being an angry teenager seemed a plausible explanation. My parents divorced that year.

I was 15 years old when my journey into mental illness officially began. I was taken to the psychiatrist. The doctor asked me questions about my interactions with my parents and friends—nothing else. I was given several tests, including the Rorschach, and subsequently, diagnosed.

The doctor told me what was wrong with me.
I was clinically depressed.

I was medicated with anti-depressants and tranquilizers. I began seeing a counselor. The counselor's name was Don Frederick. He was 30 years old and very cool. I loved him. I wanted to be a counselor just like him. He died that year while he was out running. He had some rare heart problem. I was devastated.

Breathing became difficult and I started having panic attacks. The doctor said I had psycho-somatic asthma and that I was causing myself to hyperventilate. The year before, when I was 14, I had been raped. I didn't tell anyone it happened. I was too afraid. I thought it was my fault. I pretended to myself I didn't care as a way of dealing with the shame I felt. I didn't know how to handle my feelings. Nothing seemed safe.

There were many instances where I had emotional encounters at school that brought on the convulsing sobs—like arguing with my best friend or my boyfriend. Because I could drive, I left school when I couldn't stop crying. It was as though I was trapped on a never ending rollercoaster that would stop for moments, and take off again without warning. Slowly, I became more shy and withdrawn. I was anxious, depressed and began to rebel.

3

In college, physically things were about the same as they had been in my earlier years. I had bouts of diarrhea, constipation, vomiting, earaches—the list goes on and on. I used to laugh and say, "I should own stock in Pepto Bismol." I took it often for diarrhea. I had Pepto stashed everywhere—even in the glove compartment of my car. My doctors couldn't find anything *physically* wrong with me, so they said my symptoms were psycho-somatic. It had to be true that I was psychologically damaged.

At the age of 19, I started getting big blockages in my vision that lasted for three months at a time. I was unable to see directly in front of me out of one of my eyes. I was taken to a nationally renowned specialist in Houston, who said it was Ophthalmic Migraine—definition: unexplainable. I was told I had a condition like that of an elderly person. This particular illness resembled macular degeneration. The doctor also said,

"Don't get too stressed, honey."

This issue occurred two times in my sophomore year. Both times, I was given 3 months worth of cortisone for the unexplainable condition which eventually cleared up—except for the remaining "floaters and spots" which obscure my vision to this day.

My grades were still hit or miss. I made A's or F's—there was little middle ground. I could not figure out what was wrong with me, nor did I have any explanation for my poor performance. I watched my friends graduate and begin working. I couldn't even get a college degree. I never could measure up.

For the life of me, I couldn't understand why things in my life seemed so bad. Yes, I was raped and I had the usual parental complaints (they didn't understand me, they got divorced, etc), but *really*....there had to be something else that would explain my incessant anxiety. I lived with anxiety most of my life, and as I got older it became crippling. When I wasn't hiding at home and crying, I was angry and righteous. You can't believe the amount of tears a 110 pound human being can cry. Had I blocked out some other incident, one that was even more horrific?

4

I brought the same issues into my adult life that I had when I was growing up. I was constantly on guard. Flashes of anger always led to uncontrollable tears. Sometimes the tears were helpful; *people would leave me alone*. Many times I could not maintain control and felt humiliated beyond description. I lost more than a few relationships having those kinds of reactions. I distracted myself with college life and married at the age of 21. I tried to change myself all the time. We moved before I graduated, so I quit college and told myself I really didn't know what I wanted to do. That marriage lasted almost 2 years.

During these years I was working as a dental assistant. One time I handed the doctor the wrong instrument. He shoved the instrument back into my hand furiously, then snatched the correct one from the tray. I was mortified. I ran from the room. Somehow I managed to get to the bathroom before bursting into tears. For two hours, I stayed in there sobbing and vomiting. The doctor stood outside the door, apologizing and begging me to come out. The only way out was past him. In order to go home I had to walk past my coworkers and the patients in the waiting room, with my face completely swollen from crying. I quit that job the next morning. I began taking only temporary dental assisting jobs.

I quickly tumbled into another marriage, convincing myself that I was on the right track for me. I returned to college, choosing a different major. We moved shortly thereafter and I started back to school at the college I left during my first marriage. I went to work for a CPA—my new chosen career. I often overslept and would call in sick. I had no energy and couldn't wake up or find any sort of get-up-and-go. I lost my job as a result of absenteeism. I took a secretarial job I could do from home part time.

By 25, I had such chronic stomach aches that I had an upper and lower gastro intestinal exam. I was diagnosed with a pre-ulcerous duodenum, and was told it was caused by anxiety. The gastroenterologist said,

"Try not to be so uptight, honey."

"Don't take everything so seriously. Don't take *yourself* so seriously. You need to relax, have some fun. You're young. This is the time of your life." I followed the doctor's orders to the best of my ability, but lived my life through gritted teeth.

I told myself again and again I was trying to figure out what I really wanted to do in life. Anyone who tried to push me into an answer about school, or who demanded performance from me, had to go. I systematically cut people out of my life—both family and friends. Some held on longer than others. I could not perform at a level that was expected of me and I had no explanation for being so horribly inadequate. I was riddled with panic, crying all the time and could not get anything done. I couldn't keep my house clean. Studying was impossible. It wasn't long before I quit college altogether.

I continued to withdraw from the world. I began acting aloof and was seen as being cold and abrupt. It was easier on me for people to think I was a 'bitch' rather than someone who was unstable and might completely lose it, crying uncontrollably in public. I had no control over what would bring the tears on, and they wouldn't usually stop until I was exhausted. I even had a therapist say, "You're just not a very happy person, are you, Carolyn?" I can hear his accusing tone to this day. For me, that was a life sentence. I felt like a puppet in a strange stage play, and someone else was pulling the strings. I divorced for the second time—I was 26 years old.

I was failing—at everything.

I was desperate, exhausted, and hopeless. Life hit a new low. I attempted suicide by swallowing a bottle of codeine pills. When I woke up I was really sick and scared. I called my mother and told her what I had done. She came that day and took me to a treatment center. It was another attempt, in a long line of psychological treatments, aimed at "fixing" what was wrong with me. We had high hopes that this would be the answer to what was wrong with me.

Over the next several years, I attended various therapy sessions and treatment center programs. Like a good and compliant patient, I attempted to reconnect with family that I had not seen, and work my program for recovery. While this therapy and treatment certainly did not hurt me, it in no way addressed what was wrong in my life.

Around this time, I began getting a fever every afternoon that would last into the night. This went on for about six weeks. My doctor finally put me in the hospital and I was put on IV antibiotics. Four days later, there was still no improvement. I was unhooked from the IV, and taken to an Ear, Nose, and Throat Specialist. He diagnosed me with Hay Fever. I was taken back to the hospital, spent the night, and was discharged the next day with instructions to see a local allergy doctor. After skin tests were completed and read, I was told I was highly allergic to Cedar and Juniper—which was all around where I lived. The doctor prescribed and oral medication called Guaifed. I was to take this during the winter season—when Cedar and Juniper were blooming. It relieved some of my symptoms. At least I was no longer having a fever.

5

In 1988, I took a secretarial job at Texas Tech University and returned to college. I was 28 years old. I studied Human Development and Family Studies, with the plan to get my Master's Degree in Counseling. I wanted to be like my first counselor, Don. I went to school full-time, worked full-time and white-knuckled my way through. I held on for dear life every day. I called in sick frequently, but made up for it by working on projects outside of business hours. The work I produced was exceptional, so my boss tolerated my absenteeism—to a point. It wasn't long before I was nearly fired for missing work, *again*. I missed lots of classes, but was able to make good grades. I didn't have to study much because counseling came naturally to me.

After all, I did spend 13 years in therapy and
5 weeks in a treatment center.

In 1990, I became pregnant. I was now 29. I continued working and going to school full-time. I was *so sick*. I threw up every day. Every part of my body hurt. I had shin splints so bad that I kept my legs wrapped during my entire pregnancy. I slept during lunch. I slept after work, before I went to my night classes. I slept all weekend. I was so exhausted; I honestly don't know how I survived. In my eighth month, I could barely walk.

My doctor said that, if I were his wife, he would want me to have a C-section. I agreed to this procedure. I was given a spinal tap (spinal anesthesia) so that I could be awake for the birth of my son. I'm very sensitive to sedatives and would have slept for days had I been given general anesthesia. It took five attempts to get the spinal in. I was told I had the spine of an eighty-year-old woman; they said I should be checked for that condition. I had a bad reaction to the spinal anesthesia, and my son and I were required to stay in the hospital for five days.

When my son was born, he had thrush—a yeast infection in the mouth. Since I was nursing, we passed the infection back and forth. What was supposed to be an important nurturing and bonding time was incredibly painful for me. I was drained all the time and was afraid my son was not getting enough nourishment. This was not the same experience my friends reported to have while nursing. I was only able to nurse for six weeks—another major disappointment in my life.

I wanted to be a mother more than anything in the world, and nothing about the experience of "being a mother" turned out the way I dreamed. My son's dad and I chose not marry. I wasn't able to deliver my son naturally. I wasn't able to nurse for the recommended period of time. Nothing in my life resembled how I had been raised.

15

Nothing about this fit my dreams about how life was supposed to go. I was already failing as a mom and he was a newborn baby.

One month after my son was born; I began school again full-time and returned to work part-time. At the end of May I resigned from my job and, from June until December, took thirty-six hours in college. I graduated in December of 1992. During my son's first year, when I became too exhausted, my friends would come and get my son so I could sleep. Everyone around me said I was so tired because I was a single mother and that you just don't sleep the first two years—all plausible explanations for the exhaustion. I knew it was more than that.

I knew something was wrong with me. I had an MRI because I wasn't able to walk right. I was given cortisone shots in my hip and wrist because they hurt so much. I was told I had pregnancy arthritis. I had to manage one-handed with an infant, wearing a splint to keep my wrist stabilized. I was in so much pain all the time.

Terror was beginning to creep in.

I frequently took my son to my Dad's house on weekends. I would then go into town to a friend's house and sleep for 18 hours at a time. I was so depleted. My family thought I didn't want to spend time with them, and accused me of taking advantage. It wasn't true. I just had nothing to give.

I never told the truth about what I was doing because I had been called "lazy bones" and a "sleepy head" my whole life. I was so scared I was an inadequate mother. My ex-husband told me I would be a lousy mother because I was so lazy and slept all the time—I was terrified he was right.

6

I began my Master's Program in January of 1993. I got a job at Shades of Hope Treatment Center and began fulfilling my counseling internship requirements as a treatment team member. During team meetings, the psychiatrist would often ask to see the report on a patient's lithium levels. She would frequently say the lithium needed to be increased or decreased. I didn't know what lithium levels were, but I was convinced this had to be the answer which had been eluding me my whole life! I knew a phlebotomist personally and asked him to test my lithium levels. I was quite embarrassed when he came back and asked me if I was taking lithium. The lab work showed nothing (one must be *taking* lithium for it to show up on a blood test). My blood work always showed I was healthy.

Desperation doesn't show up on a blood test.

I graduated with my Master's Degree in the spring of 1994. I was 32 years old and it was becoming more difficult to hide how sick I was. I never told anyone on the treatment team what was happening in my life, especially not the psychiatrist. I was terrified someone would find out that I really *wasn't well* and I would lose my job. I had a toddler I was responsible for—I was petrified.

About six months after graduating, I was diagnosed with double walking Pneumonia and was hospitalized for a week. During that stay, I was given many breathing treatments containing Albuterol and IV antibiotics. The sinus pain I had was not being relieved, so a dentist was called in to drain my sinuses. He gave me injections in the roof of my mouth. He then drilled holes through my mouth into my sinus cavities so everything could be flushed through with saline. He was perplexed when nothing came out. I was discharged with prescriptions for oral antibiotics and steroid inhalers.

I began to call in sick more and more often. When I was "sick," I slept. How in the world did I think I was ever going to help other people when I couldn't even show up for work? Reading began to be difficult. When I could read, I would read the Diagnostic & Statistical Manual of Mental Disorders (DSMIII at the time) looking for answers. According to the DSMIII, I was depressed. All I knew was I had random bouts of depression, slept for 18 hours, and would pop up as though nothing happened in the first place.

The "depressed times" were happening more often. I couldn't be counted on to be consistent. To be a counselor, *I knew* I had to be able to show up for the people I was serving. I couldn't figure out what was wrong with me, so I told the biggest lie of my life. I told everyone I couldn't tolerate listening to people talk about their lives all day long. I knew people couldn't rely on me.

Every sense I had <u>hurt</u> all the time.

19

I hurt too much to help anyone. Light *hurt*. Sound *hurt*. Smell *hurt*. Touch *hurt*. My clothes *hurt*. Driving *hurt*. *EVERYTHING HURT*. The only time I felt relief was when I slept.

I continued frantically searching for *the* diagnosis that would fit me. Many of the diagnoses I learned about *seemed* to fit me. What other possible diagnoses might fit? When I was at work, I would go in the bathroom, cry, and often times vomit. Was I anorexic? Was I bulimic?

I was working at an *eating disorder treatment center*, and *vomiting in the bathroom* for heaven's sake. My boss thought I was anorexic, because I was so skinny. I damn sure didn't tell her that I threw up frequently. I didn't throw anything up, I just wretched. My mind would race; panic set in—my anxiety was through the roof. Before I could be fired for absenteeism, I quit my job. I began a life-coaching business and joined a private practice as an intern for licensure.

7

I became very depressed, agitated, and was not sleeping. I was 36 years old and, as far as I was concerned, my life was a complete disaster. I called the psychiatrist I worked with at the treatment center, and told her what my symptoms were. She told me to come to Dallas the next day and she would check me into the hospital. Her partner was a specialist in manic depression and that's what she thought I had. That drive to Dallas was the most miserable drive of my life. I cannot begin to describe the horror I felt.

There is nothing more petrifying than thinking
you are losing your mind.

I had a Master's Degree in counseling, and I was being locked into a psychiatric unit. Everything I fought so hard for, everything I was supposed to *be* in life was slipping away. When I looked in the mirror, I didn't recognize my own reflection. After the usual intake questions, my new doctor asked how long I would sleep if I were left alone. I answered that I would sleep 18 hours. He said, "Bingo! That's the correct answer! You're manic-depressive." According to him, my agitation counted as the "manic" part of my diagnosis and it so happened that I was on the more "depressive" end of the manic depression scale. (Soon after this hospitalization the DSMIV was released and the diagnosis was re-labeled as bi-polar disorder). I was medicated with Lithium, and became educated about lithium levels. I learned that lithium levels appear only when you're *taking* lithium. I now understood my earlier mistake with the phlebotomist.

In that first meeting with my doctor, I begged to not attend group therapy. I could not for the life of me figure out how I was to be a brand new counselor *and* a mental patient all at the same time. He vehemently disagreed with me and told me that the only way I would get well was to become a "good patient." He then began to educate me on how to be a "good patient."

He told me he had colleagues that dealt with having a mental illness and the key to success was for me to be a "good patient." That meant: go to group, participate in therapy, and take my medication. Death would have been easier. I felt like my skin was being peeled off.

The person I thought myself to be disappeared.

Ultimately, I was a good girl and behaved myself. In order to get out quickly, I became the "good patient" he asked for. He discharged me one week later, with a list of books to read and websites to visit regarding bi-polar disorder. The doctor was certain I could live a fully functional life with the diagnosis he had given me. I left the hospital feeling rested and resolved to get better. "Getting better" did not happen. I was not better.

My view of myself continued to crumble. I became a diagnosis. I *was* mentally ill. I was no longer hard-headed and annoyingly independent. I was sick—No. Worse—I WAS MENTALLY ILL. I didn't *have* something no one wants to *have*...

I was *something no one wants to* BE. *I was Bipolar.*

8

Now my doctor only wanted to see me with a family member present. He said that bi-polar people had a habit of thinking they were fine when, in fact, they were not. As a result, what I had to say about myself and my life lost its relevance to my doctor, and my sense of "me" was further diminished. I did everything he said for me to do for five long years, because I was determined to get well even though he said I never would. I became a hyper-vigilant patient.

In the first year of treatment, I became highly agitated many times. These were considered manic episodes by my doctor. He said this was a result of taking medications not recommended for bi-polar people. For example, in the winter, I took Guaifed for my allergies. Evidently that was a no, no. "Bi-polar people can't ever take that kind of medicine," my doctor said. I had another episode when I got sick with bronchitis and was given a breathing treatment with Albuterol. I had quite a reaction. When I spoke with my doctor about it, he reprimanded me for using Albuterol, treating me as though I were a little child.

He told me every manic episode brought me closer and closer

to never-ending madness.

I learned as much as I could about the illness, and what I could and could not take. I purchased a watch with an alarm so I would never miss my medication time, no matter where I was or what I was doing. Day after day, week in and week out; month after month, and year after year—until one year melted into the next—I took my medications on time. The medications came and went; my life stayed stagnant. There were times I was so heavily medicated I could barely move. I can still remember the salty taste of lithium.

In my younger years I was a voracious reader and I desperately missed being able to read with ease. While on the medication, I would have to read sentences over and over and over. Eventually, I would throw the book down in frustration. I cannot begin to express the depths of the terror I felt. The experience in and of itself was enough to make someone go "mad."

I watched other people in therapy groups and transformative courses move beyond their past experiences. *I never could.* When one grows up with a lack of self-esteem, and most certainly a lack of self-respect, all kinds of terrible things become possible. I got into several damaging and abusive relationships. These relationships colored how I saw myself. No matter how much therapy or how many great courses I took, I *could not* seem to get over the damage that had been done. I had ugly things happen to me that no one should ever have to experience. I was given date rape drugs, which resulted in horrifying side effects, and was abused. My memory is very foggy during that time.

25

I continued to find proof for what an ineffective human being I really was. The painful memories were always around the corner, ready to rear up without a moment's notice. What kind of a mother continues to get herself into such reckless and dangerous situations?

My family and friends would talk with me, beg me to let the past go, get fed up and ultimately pull away. I couldn't blame them. I would have gotten away from myself if I could have. I was stuck with me. I couldn't stop recounting the victimizations, nor could I stop crying about them. I thought I was damaged. Why else would I not be able to move on?

I could never seem to let go of what happened to me.

I had been to treatment, 12-step programs, group therapy, had years of individual therapy, saw the priest, went to church retreats, attended bible study, prayer groups and transformational courses. I saw shamans, psychics, Reiki masters, laser light therapists, massage therapists, chiropractors, and even tried colonics—nothing worked. I gathered an extensive library that included medical dictionaries, self-help books, diet books, spiritual books, and inspirational books. I looked, and looked, and looked for answers.

9

Every time I looked at my beautiful son, my heart would sink. I was failing him miserably. During his early life, I spent so much time sick and I was so sad that it felt like someone was cutting my heart into tiny pieces. Other people did things with him—the things I wanted to do. I bet I told him a trillion times that I was sorry, I couldn't—I was sick—maybe tomorrow. He was really good about it; so good that I felt crushed. I made it to his important school functions, barely. It was the regular life activities that I missed like going to the movie or shopping or swimming.

Within a year of joining the private practice, I was too sick to work consistently so I resigned. As a result, I lost my counseling internship hours. I referred my life coaching clients to another coach and closed my business. I was too sick to keep it all together. People could not count on me. My life became very self-focused.

I was failing miserably at living a "grown-up" life.

I got a job cleaning houses—with a Master's Degree. I was devastated. I acted like it was what I wanted until I figured out what to do with my life. My heart was shattering. I wasn't the person I wanted to be and nothing I tried was impacting the continual

27

problem that was "Carolyn." My student loans went into default. I watched in complete horror as my "perfect credit score" disappeared. One cannot file bankruptcy on student loans. That meant that I was forever screwed. My life was officially never going to be the same. I was intelligent enough to know that. In my early college years, I had been an accounting student, and as far as I was concerned my life was now over.

Everything I stood for and believed in began a downward slide—desperation was at an all time high. I couldn't concentrate for a minute. The only thing I was useful at was cleaning houses. I cleaned the bathrooms and floors, while my boss did the other less physical parts because her back was hurt. My world continued to shrink. Friends began to disappear. I slowly retreated from life.

I stopped attending church and my church's Cursillo Group. I could not tolerate movies, television or music anymore—it was all too loud. I stopped using a checking account because of the risk of overdraft. I cashed my checks and lived that way. I bought convenience store food and big Diet Cokes. I spent fifteen percent of what I earned each day doing that—it was the norm for people like me. What did it matter? I wasn't ever going to have anything again anyway—my student loans were in default.

I was a default.

Everything that meant something to me seemed to have been swallowed up in a medicated haze; it just took too much energy. I became an expert at covering up all my inadequacies with the outside world (not so expert where my family was concerned). I tried desperately to make everything look like it was okay. Everything was far from okay. I was so sick all the time. As usual, I could barely get out of bed. It would be impossible for me to count the hours I lay staring at the walls or the ceiling with tears rolling down my cheeks. Nothing helped.

I followed my doctor's instructions to the very best of my ability. I continued to cry all the time and when pushed about anything, would lash out in anger. I hated myself. Every day that I woke up the first thing I thought was, "I wish I were dead." I couldn't for the life of me figure out what I had done to deserve such never-ending misery. Why was I not getting better? I was being a good patient, yet nothing changed. At night, I begged God to let me die—that seemed to be the only way out of my endless nightmare.

10

Between being heavily medicated and having a diagnosis of bi-polar disorder, Emergency Room visits were horrendous. On the occasions I went to the ER, no matter my complaint, all they wanted to know was if I had taken my medications. They didn't see *me*, they couldn't hear *me*—all they saw was my diagnosis. The very minute I began to speak, I could see the nurse's, then the doctor's eyes glaze over, waiting for me to finish talking so they could prescribe something and get me out of there.

As a result of my diagnosis, clinicians expected me to "act" erratic and unstable. Whether I acted that way or not, I was treated like I might come unhinged at any moment. I am a well-educated, well-mannered articulate woman. I behave appropriately in public or I *do NOT* go out. Poor behavior was not allowed in my family—it would have never been permitted. The times I felt I could not control myself, I did not leave my house. I would have died first. My being well-behaved had nothing to do with how physically sick and emotionally miserable I was all the time.

I felt as though I lived in a refrigerator box with holes cut out for eyes that I could look through. On a good day, I was all the way up to the holes looking out. Most days, I could only see light from the back of the box. These are the times I refer to as "living life through gritted teeth." It was like I had to drag myself around by my own hair, through the muck and mire, forcing myself to do what "normal" people do like cook, clean, pick my child up from school, and hold a conversation with someone.

One time I was in the emergency room after having the stomach flu, my tongue was black—no doubt from the medication and dehydration. While speaking to the ER nurse and doctor, I specifically told them all of the types of medication my psychiatrist said I could not take as a result of my diagnosis. It was vital that I not take anything that might alter my mood in any way. On my way out, I was handed a prescription for Phenergan. This was explicitly against my doctor's orders.

I felt invisible.

No one listened to me, no one heard me.

Everything in our medical, psychiatric and psychological education has taught us that mental illness is an unchangeable fact. I understand the misconceptions and misinterpretations that can occur when someone is labeled as mentally ill. I also understand the difficulties those diagnoses present.

Deep and dark is the hole called mental illness. Darker still, is when others found out I had been diagnosed as mentally ill. The label of mental illness told a story about me, and then I was stuck living that story. The diagnosis colored the view I had of myself and the way others saw me. Though I struggled to overcome this view, more often than not, I failed. The point is my diagnosis spoke for me. It spoke louder than my own voice.

It was as though I were being silenced.

I experienced a complete loss of agency—*a loss of self.* The diagnosis replaced my identity. During my life, I have been in some very terrifying situations, yet watching people not listen to me was more terrifying than anything I ever experienced.

11

After five years with my psychiatrist, two hospitalizations and no improvement, I took matters into my own hands. I quit utilizing all medical services, except to have my medication refilled. Slowly, over a course of 3 years, I weaned myself off the psychiatric medications without telling anyone. I would get the medication refilled and then would throw the extra pills away so no one would know what I was doing. **I do not recommend that anyone do as I did. Consult your doctor for assistance.**

Since I was not any worse than I always had been, no one seemed to notice. I still lived in a constant state of agitation but that was the same with or without medication. Thankfully, I no longer had to fight the "medication hangover," which interrupted simple functions like thinking for myself, or reading, or basic desire for engaging in life. I was back to my regular levels of anxiety and depression, so life was "normal" for me.

Somewhere in all of this I met someone who was able to see "me." For the life of me, I don't know how. We got together and within a few years, moved to another city for work. Thus began a series of promotions for my partner and subsequent moves around the country. Moving was very hard for me. I was so terrified about having to interact with new people; I could hardly breathe most of the time. I would see to all the details of the move and set up house. I got to be a stay at home mom and some days I was able to be the mom I wanted to be—sort of. I could pull this off from 3:30 to 8:30 when my son was out of school.

Many days I was irritable or I cried all the time. Mornings were difficult. I would ask my son to forgive me, to fix his own breakfast, and to let me know when it was time for me to drive him to school. On those days I would convince myself that kids need to be self-sufficient. I hated what I thought I was doing to him. I was so sick. It seems as though all I ever said to him was, "I'm sorry, I can't. I don't feel good."

The degree of self-loathing I had in my youth grew exponentially by the time my son was in middle school. I could not stand myself and it seemed as though others around me could barely tolerate me either. It was like I was living in quicksand—I couldn't trust myself to do much of anything I said I would do. I never knew if I could say yes to anything and actually be able to show up.

My rule of living became "Always Say No."

A "no" can easily be changed into a "yes." It is much more difficult to change a "yes" into a "no." It didn't help that I was merciless—I spoke brutally harsh words to myself and ultimately hated myself for living and taking up space. Dear God, I hated having to be in my skin. No one knew what life was really like for me because I had so isolated myself. My world continued to shrink.

12

I used to take my son to church and drop him off for Sunday School. On many a Sunday, I would sit in my car in the parking lot trying to convince myself that I could go in for the service. The thought of being in a closed space surrounded by people terrified me. I didn't know if I was going to have a panic attack in the middle of the service and have to leave. I made it into the building about half of the time. The rest of the time I would drive to the Jack in the Box parking lot so no one would see me. I would then cry some more and berate myself for being such a loser.

On the days I did make it inside, I would force myself to go to the Parish Hall for 15 minutes after church and talk to people; that fifteen minutes seemed like an eternity. It was devastating to me to not be able to go into church. Church was the only place I could find peace as a little girl, other than being on a horse. Attending church had become excruciating like everything else.

I hated my life. I couldn't work; I couldn't count on myself enough to return to my career in counseling. How could I go to work when I never knew whether I was going to be crying or in worse shape than my clients? It was an insidious trap. My life was a living hell.

Every day when I awoke I heard myself say,
"I wish I was dead."

Like a broken record, I heard, "I wish I was dead. I wish I was dead. I wish I was dead. I wish I was dead." It was just a matter of course for me. It was automatic—never something I had to think about; it was just there. Not, "I want to die." Not, "I'm going to kill myself." Not, "I can't take it anymore." Just, "I wish I was dead."

I would hear that over and over until I would wake up enough to argue with myself saying, "Yeah, well you're not. Get your ass out of bed. More time WILL NOT HELP. GET UP! GET UP! GET UUUPPPPP!" I started every day that way. I used to say I was beating myself into submission. I was like a General giving marching orders in my own head all the time. Barking orders at myself was what it took for me to get anything done—pick up my son from school, cook dinner, do the laundry or clean the house.

I had many coping mechanisms in place so I would look like a regular, functional, stay-at-home mom. I could go places if I wasn't alone. Being alone out in public nearly killed me. For years, I didn't go anywhere alone but to my son's school. The anxiety I felt was excruciating. I cannot count the times I left full shopping carts at the grocery store because I started to have a panic attack. I would drive home as fast as I could, get in the house, and fall on the floor just inside the door. Then the sobbing would begin. I would cry until I threw up or exhausted myself. I would then get up and try to make it look like I had done something that day.

On good days, I would go to my partner's office, do some "volunteer" job, go to lunch with the team and then throw myself out the door in time to pick up my son from school. Back then, there were times I thought my son really would be better off without me. I simply couldn't figure out how to end my life without everyone hating me, and leaving my son with damage that could not be undone.

I never really knew what was wrong with me, but I knew I better come up with an answer. If the medical doctors couldn't figure out what was wrong with me, I was going to have to figure it out another way. I searched for answers with even more desperation. There were so many times I threw myself into action on something; a new cure, answer or solution. My resolve would only last for a few days before I knew I couldn't keep it up—I knew it wouldn't turn out how I had hoped. I knew I couldn't consistently do the work required of me to accomplish anything and have it turn out successfully.

I was constantly terrified that people would discover what a fraud I was. I became quite masterful at hiding the truth—so much so that I got very lost from myself. I got into my fair share of horrible situations all the while continuing to "work" on myself. Desperate people will try anything, and I did. I studied weather patterns and charted the barometric pressure to see if that had some impact on me. I became convinced that I had done something really, really, *really* bad during my former lifetime to have deserved the hell I was living. Thinking incessant negative thoughts made life that much more unbearable. I could not stop the chatter in my head.

13

When I was 42, my family lived in Redding, California. My son was in 7th grade. We had been there for a few months when my mother came to visit. For fun we went to the local Alternative Health Fair one Sunday afternoon. It was there that I met my soon to be dear friend, Ronda. She had a booth at the fair and was selling herbs and other supplements related to general health and well-being. I went to purchase an herb that was to relieve constipation. Ronda began to ask questions about my health concerns.

There I was, standing in the middle of a health fair discussing my lack of daily bowel movement. I was really embarrassed. I had been to the doctor for this issue many times with no definitive diagnosis. Again and again, I was told to consider seeing a therapist.

Physical complaints with no medical basis are "in your head."

When no medical reason can be found, digestive problems are frequently diagnosed as a psychological issue. During the conversation, Ronda said, "Have you considered therapy?" I glared at her—I wanted to jump across the table and choke her. She quickly apologized, handed me her business card, and told me to make an appointment with her. She was a Certified Nutritional Consultant with a Master's Degree in Herbology. *I hadn't tried that yet!* The next week began a three year long journey in an attempt to crack the code of, "What in the world is wrong with Carolyn?"

Ronda started me on several supplements and I began attending a raw food course she taught. I went on a 70% raw food diet. I began to feel better and my joints didn't hurt as much. However, nothing changed for me emotionally or digestively. Throughout those years she was completing her Ph.D. in Holistic Nutrition. I think I was one of her best and most difficult "cases." We tried everything but running in the streets naked.

14

My relationship of ten years ended. We had moved back to Texas so, thankfully, I was "at home." My son, now 15 years old, was attending boarding school—family made that possible. However, I was in dire straits. I had been self-employed or unemployed for most of my adult life. I did have a few life coaching clients, yet not enough to sustain me.

I was 46 years old and had no real work resume.

I moved in with my brother's fiancé and took a job at a local dress shop. My boss repeatedly told me to lighten up and to smile—I couldn't do either. For the hundred millionth time in my life, I was told not to take things so seriously. Several years before, I had been given a coffee mug that said, "Angels have wings because they take themselves lightly." I desperately wanted to be "light." Apparently, I was not capable. I lasted in that job for three months.

Ronda and I continued our quest for answers in earnest. I'm certain she put me on speaker phone and let me ramble on, crying and bemoaning my lot in life, while she wrote her papers for school, and searched for answers to my health problems. I held on for dear life, wailing all the way.

My family members were aware that I no longer was taking medications, and were certain I needed anti-depressants. My mother was furious with me because I refused to return to the doctor and go back to taking medication. She wanted me to take something—*anything*—that would make me quit crying and get on with my life. In order for the medication to work, I had to take enough to damn near put me in a stupor, and then I couldn't think at all. The only time I would stop crying was if I took enough to make everything go numb. Medication made me feel stupid and thick-headed.

On multiple occasions, it was suggested that I see a therapist—again. *Wanna really make someone crazy?* Give them multiple mental illness diagnoses. Put them on enough drugs so they cannot think or read or follow along in social conversations. Make it so they can't wake up until about 11am, then expect them to be at work ready to go at 8am. That will do it!

I was an intelligent person, trapped in a body
with a mind that couldn't interact functionally
with the world—and I could not get out.

I had seen countless doctors for countless reasons and was given countless diagnoses and countless medications throughout my entire life. I was diagnosed with various mental illnesses. I quit seeing doctors almost completely—nothing seemed to help me. I thought there was no need to see another doctor. I was repeatedly told, "I ought to be thankful for how healthy I was." My blood work was always great except for having chronic anemia. Over and over I was told how healthy I was and yet, I had an exhaustive list of undiagnosable issues. I was so accustomed to feeling bad it was normal.

I watched my dreams for myself as an individual and as a mother turn into complete desperation and survival, covering for myself and my inadequacies at every turn. I became expert at covering up all that was missing, trying desperately to look like everything was okay.

I hated myself for continuing to indulge in hope.

Truthfully, I was angry, jealous, and resentful. I covered it up by being cheery and helpful. Underneath the cheery helpfulness was self-loathing and despair. The biggest problem I had was that I took up space and thought I contributed nothing to life. I hated my life. *Did I say I hated my life?* I hated the fact that I continued to wake up every day and breathe. Being seen as a problem and as a "taker" in society did something to me and my view of the world. Mostly, I was deeply saddened.

I had become damaged—subhuman—a drain on my family and society. I slid into self-loathing. I watched others watch me with a distrustful eye.

15

By the age of 47, I rarely left my house alone—the anxiety I experienced was crippling. When I had to, I could toughen up and make it through, but it took everything I had. I became such a chameleon. I got so good at lying about things that I became a liar to myself and to the people I loved. I had no answers for what was happening to me or who I had become. It was a horrifying and miserable existence. There was no way I could function in a regular world when experiences I was having were real for me, but no one else.

I was teetering on the edge of actually taking my life.

I just couldn't take it anymore. I constantly felt sick with no medical answers and, of course, the doctors thought it was psychological—*THAT*, I no longer believed. How many years of therapy could I actually need? My story could not be dismantled; it was like a never-ending marathon tangled up with intense feelings. The older I got, the harder it was for me to put a smile on my face and go out into the world at all.

Over the years, I learned some very helpful and wonderful things, but none of it made any REAL difference *for me*. Ronda and I continued our friendship all the while looking for a solution to my health problems. I took courses that were cathartic for others—*never for me*. I would leave the weekend courses, the therapy sessions, the coaching sessions, church or church retreats with a renewed sense of, "I can do it." The "it" wouldn't last a week. There were times I didn't care, couldn't care—didn't dare to care.

Once I was diagnosed, my personal interactions changed: people either pitied me or they feared for me. It was worse when they were afraid of me—that was excruciating. I was in multiple relationships, which all failed. I lost my career. Life got worse as the years went by. I was told countless times that I should be grateful. How could I possibly be grateful when NOTHING in my life turned out the way I wanted or the way I hoped?

In my view, I was a sick and pathetic loser. I was a drain on my family financially. I couldn't pay my own way. The only reason I did not live on the streets, was because of my family. I was on welfare—it was just privately funded. I was thankful for the help, but grateful? No way. My college degrees couldn't help me, doctors couldn't help me, therapists couldn't help me and it seemed that I had been so bad that God *wouldn't* help me. For years, I begged for mercy—that didn't work either. I pled with Him to let me die. I was rapidly reaching the end of my rope. I was losing my determination. I was losing my ability to convince myself that the next thing would be the answer. I was losing my hard-headedness.

I was losing this battle. There really was no hope.

16

In February of 2009, Ronda called, and said she had a new idea. She remembered having a friend long ago who was highly allergic to gluten. If Ronda had been baking in the last week, her friend could not come over to visit. Ronda asked me to stop eating gluten and told me I would know very quickly if this was the problem. I said, "OK, but what is gluten?" I had never heard of this thing called *gluten*. She told me to stop eating bread, pasta, cookies—anything made with flour. I couldn't believe I was going to agree to try something else.

For two weeks I didn't have anything at all that was made of flour. Then I ate a sandwich. The next day, feeling agitated and irritable, I told the friend I was with that if he even looked at me funny I would start crying. He knew me well enough to know I meant it. I suddenly realized I had not felt agitated or teary the day before— or the day before. I had to sit down. I was stunned. It seemed as though the world went silent. Everything in my whole reality changed.

I found the answer I had been looking for my entire life.

17

My breath caught and my mind began to race. I reviewed the two weeks I had not eaten bread, pasta, and cookies—nothing that contained flour. I had not cried, been irritable, or riddled with anxiety. I hadn't even noticed! I ate that sandwich and all those symptoms came back in one day and *I KNEW WHY.*

The "New World" of gluten-free eating began. One by one my chronic, life-long symptoms disappeared. Systematically, I removed all gluten products from my diet. Learning to remove all gluten products was not an easy task, yet it was essential to my getting well.

Early on in my journey of going gluten free I woke up itching, feeling out of sorts and in an instant I *knew* without a shadow of a doubt what was happening. *I knew* I had eaten something that contained gluten. It seems odd, but one does not notice the removal of symptoms as much as one notices their return. This was an important thing for me to know.

A certain amount of time passed before I noticed any changes at all. The symptoms which disappeared rapidly returned when I ate something containing gluten. Within a day, I would be panicky, itchy, bitchy, crying, and, again, having to force myself to get out of the house. Discovering what was causing my illnesses became a new problem. I would get clear and have an accident; get clear and have an accident. This went on for months. I felt like I was in a mine field of food.

During the first months of gluten-free living, Ronda sent me some supplements. They were to help heal my intestinal lining from the damage she was certain had been done. I received the supplements in the mail, took them, and within hours was getting a familiar stomach ache. The supplements contained gluten. Neither one of us thought to look at the ingredients. I remember sobbing to her on the phone saying I was only going to eat lettuce and drink water for the rest of my life. During that call, she talked about a possible diagnosis of celiac disease and what would be required from me in order to obtain an accurate diagnosis.

I had no health insurance.

I could not get health insurance.

I had been hospitalized for mental illness.

I was denied all major medical policies.

I was not going to have the test required.

I have often said that things are simple, yet not easy. This is the opposite. Going gluten free is easy—yet is not simple. Gluten is everywhere and can be found in almost everything. I had little reserve to deal with every accidental infraction. Education in an area of study completely foreign to me began—the study of food label reading.

Food label reading should come with its own Ph.D.

49

18

In the early summer of 2009, I was still barely functioning. I was NOT crying or full of anxiety. I just felt sick. My son was away for the summer, working as a camp counselor. Around this time, my grandmother had a really bad fall. I went back to my hometown to help my grandparents. I spent the summer at a family home and only left the house to see my grandparents, have lunch or dinner with my parents, and go to the grocery store. I had the privilege of driving my grandmother to all her favorite stores and to her appointments. It was easy for me to go at her pace, because I was moving at exactly the same speed—she was 87 years old.

My grandmother told me of a book she had seen on *The View* entitled "*The G Free Diet: A Gluten Free Survival Guide,*" by Elisabeth Hasselbeck. I purchased it immediately and read the whole book that night. I learned how to take care of myself. I learned what to watch for and to have "safe" food with me.

I learned to always be prepared.

This book became the roadmap which helped me navigate an entirely new way of living. For a person who felt overwhelmed, it was an easy book to read. I found other books on the subject of gluten free living which were also helpful. Some books contained way too much information to be useful for me at the time. I learned to stick with simplicity.

Most of my time that summer was spent learning how to prepare gluten free or "clean" meals—*meals without processed food of any kind*. It took time to incorporate a whole new way of cooking and eating into my daily life. I began to double my recipes and freeze meals, so I would always have something "clean" that was ready for me to eat. I learned how to cook what my body *needed*.

**The more "clean" I became, the more relief
I felt—mind, body and spirit.**

I began to develop a relationship with my mother that had never before been possible. For many years, she was led astray with the movement of "tough love." It didn't help that a psychiatrist once told her people don't have breakdowns unless there is someone there to care for them—indicating that if no one is watching people do just fine. However, once I discovered some real answers that were consistently helping me, she started to listen in a new way.

During that summer, I only had three "accidents" with my food. I was clear headed enough to notice my symptoms return when I was glutened. The symptoms follow a specific progression for me: for two days, my skin itches and I become irritable; for the next day or so, I feel extremely blue and so thick-headed that I can hardly think;

for the next two days, I cry at the drop of a hat or even worse, sob uncontrollably—depending on what is happening. Then, miraculously, it is over. This progression of symptoms happens each and every time I get glutened.

Knowing what to expect gives me freedom.

Knowing that I've had an accident does not keep the symptoms at bay. I *will* become irritable. I *will* get foggy headed. I *will* cry. I cannot 'convince' myself to act differently. However, I can tell people in my life what's happening, what day I'm on, and how much longer it will be before I'm feeling better. It's so easy now. I don't chase my tail trying to figure out why I'm irritable or sad. I just wait it out and people don't have to worry about me anymore. I know exactly how long the experience and symptoms will last.

19

By the fall of 2009, my health was steadily improving. I began to look at my life through the lens of an *actual, physical illness* rather than a mental illness and all the associated psychological symptoms. I started to see an entirely different picture. I often sat and stared out the window, reviewing periods of my life again and again. I was staggering from the effects of the life I had lived. Making sense of my life from this new perspective was a daunting task.

The simple fact that *I felt better* was new to me. I didn't recognize myself. Daily, I was surprised to wake up clear headed. I was shocked that I was not crying. I no longer needed to take naps. I was now awake all day—*every day*. I talked to my friends on the phone a lot about this new experience of living. My mother was right there to support me. I would not have made it through this without all of them. I am deeply grateful for the time they spent with me.

I began walking for exercise. At first, I walked two-tenths of a mile (half a block). Very soon, I was walking several miles a day. Slowly, I was coming out of the quicksand I had been stuck in all of my life. It was as though I was learning to walk on solid ground for the first time.

People often exclaim, "Oh how awful that you can't eat bread or cookies!" I very happily say, "What was awful was crying all the time and not being able to freely leave my house. Now *that* was awful!" I have no desire whatsoever to give any more days to the *gluten monster*—it ate enough of my life.

I never have the experience of waking up and saying, "Hmmm. I would like to eat pancakes, a sandwich and some cookies; then I'll spend the next five or six days of my life paying for having eaten it." There is not a cookie or piece of bread in this world that's worth that price to me.

Eating gluten costs me my *LIFE.* It costs me my *ALIVENESS.* It costs me my *VITALITY* and my *CONNECTION* to people. It costs me my participation in the world and will send me right back into solitary confinement. No thank you!

NOT eating those foods is NOT a problem for me!

20

I spent the first year of this process learning how to eat gluten-free. I do *everything* in my power to avoid an accident. Still, I had at least one accident a month in the beginning. Sometimes I couldn't tell until the itching started. I would "go back in the hole" and wait it out, complaining mightily. Now when I have an accident, it's as simple and as inconvenient as having a really bad cold.

Once when I was staying at a friend's apartment, I was taking my morning walk and the maintenance men began to mow. Instantly, I held my breath—mowed grass had always meant asthma in the past. I paused for a moment, and then took a deep breath. *Nothing happened.* I finished my walk quickly, went back to the apartment and began to cry. *I cried with relief*, because I was breathing freely.

Over time, the distance between "glutenings" grew. I could not believe all the symptoms, to which I was so accustomed, were rapidly disappearing. I began to sleep better at night and wake up refreshed. I had never awakened ready to get up in my whole life! I didn't have restless legs. I didn't have difficulty breathing. I didn't have stomach aches. I was no longer crippled by anxiety. I no longer cried uncontrollably. I didn't live in a chronically agitated state. It was the strangest experience.

At times my progress felt terribly slow—it had to be slow. For years I had spent most of my time alone. I had been coaching clients over the phone. I was not accustomed to being with people physically. My circle of friends and activities began to expand. I was socializing easily, but I had my limits. It took me a while to work up to spending a whole day with people, without my getting squirrely. Occasionally, the reality of my discovery felt overwhelming.

It took more than a year to become comfortable
with this new found freedom.

Day by day I watched with wonder as I began to be able to count on myself in ways I never had. I began to laugh and it wasn't forced. I would go to the grocery store and sometimes be shocked that I was there and hadn't had to force myself to go. I often said yes to invitations early, because I *knew* I would be able to attend. I was surprised to find myself freely doing things without all the self-berating I had done my whole life.

It was astounding to review my life and know that so much of my past was due to my body's reaction to gluten. The diagnoses I received, the illnesses I had, my inability to work consistently, or maintain a relationship, was all because of a reaction to food.

21

After I was gluten free for a year, I knew I could count on myself to perform the jobs that were expected of me. I began to take on more coaching clients. I still didn't feel as well as I thought I should be feeling. I couldn't quite figure it out, but at least I wasn't crying and I was leaving the house with ease. I met a wonderful new friend named Leisa, who shared her doctor's name with me. I went to see the doctor with great trepidation (remember, I refused to go to doctors anymore unless I thought I might die from something). I discussed my physical symptoms only. I had a full physical. Regular blood work was ordered as well as a food allergy panel. I was to return in three weeks for the results.

The results were shocking! The test confirmed I was intolerant to gluten. I was also highly reactive to yeast and eggs. I was milk intolerant. The list goes on and on. I also had a bad case of Candida (a systemic yeast infection). An entire list of food was to be removed from my diet. I was put on an extremely strict, three-month-long, rotation diet.

Family and friends were so happy for me to finally have discovered real, definitive answers about my health. I was grateful to have the answers, but was now dealing with the very real toll food had taken on my life. I was livid! It was hard for them to understand why I was angry, so I kept to myself for a while.

I could NOT believe foods were the cause of my misery.

I had been medicated and treated psychologically for 32 years of my life and _it was food._ I felt sick in an entirely different way. My mind raced across memories—time lost, years lost, dreams lost, relationships lost, mothering lost, money lost, career lost. _IT WAS FOOD?_ It was food.

IT WAS FOOD!

22

I went into a funk at that point. It had only been a year since I took gluten out of my diet. I had begun to have a life—I was doing things with friends. Things included going out to eat, like people do. It started to feel like I was now going to be a social freak. I mean really, who would want to hang out with someone that was such high-maintenance?

I followed the doctor's orders without fail, which meant I rarely left my apartment for meals. I became afraid of food. It was as though part of my mind melted—everything I ever knew or had ever been taught about food changed. It was quite a ride. I had great support from family and implemented the new plan.

For the first time in my life, the doctor's promise that I would soon feel better became a reality. She said I would feel dramatically better in about two weeks, and I did. My head began to *really* clear. I was able to think about things I wanted to think about. I began to read easily. Slowly, but surely, I got my feet underneath me. I learned how to go to restaurants and ask questions about the menu. I began to advocate for my specific needs.

I began to get my voice back—my own sense of personal power.

I was actually beginning to speak up and ask for what I needed. Asking for what one needs is a vital part of a healthy life and I was doing it. I kept it all slow and steady.

23

During the second year of living gluten free and removing all the foods I had sensitivity or intolerance to, I noticed that familiar ways of behaving and reacting to life had changed. I used to be hyper-vigilant and always jumpy. That hyper-vigilance disappeared. In most situations, I knew how I was going to react. All of those patterns simply disappeared. Almost everything I knew about myself changed. I did not shrink if someone was upset with me. I simply listened and worked it out—I did not cry!

One weekend my aunt and I were staying together at a friend's apartment. She burst in the bathroom while I was in the shower. She yelled, "Hey, I'm going down to my car. I'll be right back." Previously, I would have dropped to my knees from fright. *Nothing happened.* I stood there in shock. I was shocked because nothing happened. Then I cried. I cried because *nothing happened.* Crying was rare for me now! Again and again, I would tell myself, "This is really true. This is really happening. I am steady. I am stable." I scarcely recognized myself. It was a very strange experience.

It takes time to get to know oneself as
an entirely different person.

After removing gluten, my analytical thinking returned. For most of my adult life, I could not keep up with technological advances nor did I have a sense of direction. In the "glutened" years, the most I could do was write an email or a word document. Bit by bit, I began to learn how to do things on my phone or on the computer, simply because it made sense to me. I purchased an iPhone and I began to use it without too much of a transitional struggle. My personal coaching business increased and I handled the expansion well.

I was referred to a wellness clinic for nutritional response testing and therapy. I began to use a food journal and take specific supplements for healing my intestinal lining. The protocol at this clinic was beneficial to me, and I experienced great results. I learned how to manage the surges in my blood sugar and my mood stabilized even more. I began taking yoga classes and continued walking at least two miles a day. I also began to see a practitioner who specializes in endocrinology. He addressed the issues I had with my menstrual cycle and my thyroid. It wasn't long before my energy and ability to focus increased. Overall, I felt better than ever. It was amazing.

The following year, I accepted a contract with a company that provides workshops focused on recovery from mental illness. For 18 months, we traveled all over Texas providing workshops to groups at State Hospitals and Community Mental Health Centers. I did not call in sick one time. I learned how to travel and stay well. It may seem funny, but I *felt normal*–I had never felt "normal" in my life.

24

At times, I get frustrated by the impact food has had on my finances and my career. However, I have a new found ability to let go of the past. Before, I could never stop going on about the things that had happened to me. I could never let anything go. I shudder when I think of how life used to be for me; it is nothing like that now. My past no longer runs my life. I live in the present and look forward to my future. It is a black and white, day and night difference.

If I have an accident with gluten, it is wonderful to be able to tell those closest to me what to expect from me for the next week. It is surreal. One wrong bite and I am miserable for a week. Then, as if by magic, I am fine and happy again. It never changes. It is like knowing the sun is going to come up—and so am I.

The last gluten accident I had, my mother said, "Oh, I'm so sorry honey. Call me when you are better." She and I both know there is nothing to do but wait for the symptoms to go away. My friends know there is nothing to do but wait. My business partner knows. I am able to reschedule clients if they are scheduled on the crying days. I get to do it well in advance of their appointment. I get to tell the truth—I am sick. I don't have to explain why or with what—I'm just sick—it's like having the flu. It's a rare occasion that I reschedule anything anymore.

Sometimes I am moved to tears just because I wake up at dawn and lay peacefully in the quiet. Early in the morning, the world is quiet and so is my mind. I am so very thankful to *know* that I have become a person that can be counted on; to *know* I will communicate responsibly with others; and to *know* I can have regular feelings like sadness and anger without those feelings taking over. I love *knowing* when I experience "strong" emotions, I have the ability to pause, collect my thoughts, and choose to speak or not. I get to choose today. I am in charge today.

I am joyfully living my life. I didn't even know what joy was. I can make plans and I am able to keep them—barring unforeseen circumstances—just like other people. I can handle life's never-ending challenges—even when it seems really hard. I wake up easily. I have the energy to do the things required of me. When I go to bed at night, I say my prayers and thankfully look forward to the next day.

I love the relationship I have with my son. He is amazed by the changes in me. I asked him how he thought I was doing. He said, "I'm not afraid to hug you anymore." I asked him what he meant, saying I didn't know he had been afraid. He said, "Yeah, I used to be scared I would break you, you felt so fragile to me." He was 19 years old when he said that—it was heart wrenching and joyful at the same time.

I am able to be who I always wanted to be. I am able to utilize the skills I learned during the years I was sick. I am able to consistently implement the training and education I have received.

There are still many parts of my life I dream of resurrecting or renewing; those parts are well on their way. I can see a future developing that was never possible before.

I am actually happy.

Part Two

Amy

I was in the sixth grade when I realized I wasn't like everyone else. I couldn't *be happy* like other people around me. I couldn't find the words for answers when people asked me questions. It was difficult for me to express myself and to share how I felt without crying. I did everything I could to keep the tears from flowing. I learned to be quiet about what I was dealing with and how I felt about things. Life was a constant struggle; it hurt to be in my skin. I used to cry myself to sleep at night asking God why I was so different than everyone else.

Hanging out with my friends was excruciating at times. I watched others around me laugh, play, and goof around. I always felt like I was looking in from the outside. Why couldn't I be happy? Why couldn't I answer simple questions? All I wanted to do was cry and jump in a hole to hide. I looked anywhere and everywhere for ways to numb my feelings. Food was my comfort.

My parents took me to the doctor. There was an answer to the way I was behaving. The problem was me. I was depressed. I was twelve years old. I was no longer Amy Leigh Pierce. I was *Amy Leigh Pierce–Depressed.* I now carried a label that would haunt me for years.

It was not apparent to the outside world, but that label changed the way my family saw me—and it changed the way I saw myself.

Depression—that simple word changed my life forever.

Once I received my initial diagnosis of depression, everything got lumped into the label. I was broken—damaged somehow, and didn't deserve to walk on this earth. Using food was the best way I knew to "numb out" the negative thoughts in my head. Bread, cookies and cake did that for me *almost instantly*. I would steal food from my friend's house or find the food that was hidden in our house which was meant for my brother. It was the only way I had to make the negative feelings stop. I was gaining weight. I learned how to act as if I was having fun, and act as if I was enjoying life, when in fact I was really miserable. Suicide attempts began early. I wanted the anxiety I was feeling to stop. I wanted the pain in my head and my body to stop. I had no way of expressing this in a way the adults around me could comprehend.

Adolescence was tough for me. I didn't want to be the way I was. It was as if a dark heavy cloud was always surrounding me. There were periods of time when it would lift, moments of joy when the light would shine through, yet for the most part life was grey. I had no real understanding of what was happening. I constantly worried about what my friends were saying about me and doing without me. I always questioned everything. I was never able to just be. Life was becoming more and more difficult. At home, I would hide for hours on end. I just wanted the whole world to go away. I started to have periods of uncontrollable emotional outbursts. When arguments would occur or strife would enter the picture, my brain would shut down. It was as if there was too much information coming in at one time and I could *never* get my words out. At times I would say anything to make the questioning stop.

One time I ran away to the office building I cleaned; I just had to get away. I needed everything to be quiet so I could think. This was the first time I remember someone outside our immediate family being called in to "deal" with me. I remember being locked in the office building, screaming, not wanting to talk to my mother or father and then all of a sudden the preacher from our church showed up. I don't remember his name, yet to this day I remember his kind soul. In the midst of all my anger and fear, I had to let him into the building. I do not remember what he said to me, but I do remember that he took me to Dairy Queen to talk everything over. I got an ice cream, a grand mix of sugar and a cake cone; then I calmed down.

2

I had always been very active playing soccer and tennis. A turning point happened when I was in the seventh grade. It was during this year that I started having trouble with my knee and went back and forth to the doctor. After months of complaints (all of which were seen as my trying to get attention), I was diagnosed with a slipped femoral epiphysis. I was immediately hospitalized and placed in traction. My hip had slipped off the growth plate and it had to be screwed in place. I felt trapped—trapped by my inability to get up and move. I started to feel overwhelmed by the thoughts and feelings I was having. It was as if I was being swallowed up. Until this point my activity level had been a superb coping mechanism. It allowed me to take out the frustration I felt on that little yellow tennis ball. *Now all I could do was lie in bed.*

**I was trapped with my thoughts and feelings
in a way I had never been before.**

Food took on an even larger role in numbing my emotions. Yet, even with food, I was losing the fight. It took more and more to numb out—more and more to hold the anxiety at bay. The outside world felt like an assault to me. I retreated into my own little world, pretending nothing was wrong. Life as I knew it changed forever, and I fell into the pit of despair. By the last six weeks of my eighth grade year, I was having lots of migraine headaches and fought with my parents frequently about going to school.

I had surgery to take the screws out of my hip during those last six weeks of the school year. I had two holes in my hip and if I was knocked down, while on crutches, my hip could break. My parents were able to arrange with the school and the doctor for me to go homebound for the rest of the school year so that I could complete the eighth grade. The real reason for this was because of my emotional issues, yet it was easily disguised as a medical necessity. It was a great cover. While that six weeks and the summer gave me some space, it did not fix anything. It didn't change the way I felt; it just gave me a way to get through the school year.

High school was not any better. I spent all my time trying to act like everyone else. If everyone was laughing I made sure I laughed too, yet I had no idea what they were laughing about. I couldn't keep up. I was able to play tennis again, but it was not the outlet it had been before.

After my freshman year, I found out we would be moving. I would have the ability to start over in a place where only a few people knew me. Those that did know me were friends from church camp. They had not been around me on a daily basis, so I was excited. What I didn't realize was that, *moving was not going to change anything.* I would be the same me. I didn't know the feelings and problems I had in Jacksonville would follow me to Nacogdoches. It wasn't long before the depression and negative thoughts overwhelmed me again. I turned to alcohol. It allowed me to sleep; my mind would slow down and be quiet. Not only was I sneak eating, I was now sneak drinking.

3

During my junior year of high school, I experienced my first psychiatric hospitalization. My mother discovered me after I attempted suicide. I couldn't quit crying. I was so tired and didn't know which way to turn. I agreed to get some help at the local private psychiatric hospital and I was quietly admitted. While I only spent a few weeks there that first time, my life forever changed.

Up until this point, family and very close friends were the only ones that knew of my struggles. I had not been to school for two and a half weeks, and had only talked to a few friends. However, I was involved in the Nacogdoches Heritage Festival and the first introduction to society at the local country club was taking place. I had it in my mind that I could attend the event and everything would be alright.

I was not prepared for what actually happened when I was released from the hospital on a pass to attend this event. While my friends were glad to see me, you could have cut the air with a knife. No one knew what to say, much less me. I couldn't tell them when I would be back at school. Now everyone knew that I had been in a psychiatric institution. I did everything I could so others would not look at me as if I were "crazy." This was my first real experience with the stigma that a mental illness diagnosis brings. The looks, the whispers behind my back, and people even saying things right to my face were bitter pills to swallow. I felt about two inches tall after that night and just wanted to disappear.

I made it through the night like I did many times before; I plastered a big smile on my face even though I felt like I was dying inside. I remember going back to the hospital after that evening and never wanting to leave. How was I going to face everyone? How was I going to go back into the "real" world and pretend like nothing happened? Everything was different. After that first hospitalization, people at school began calling me "Crazy Amy."

I now had a Scarlet Letter. Mine was an "M" for Mental.

I returned to school and endured the torment of wearing that label like never before. I walked into the girl's bathroom and found graffiti written about me on the bathroom stall. A part of me died that day; a part of my spirit broke. It didn't matter how hard I tried to fit in or how hard I worked to hide the thoughts that swirled in my head.

Everyone knew I was "crazy" and I, Amy, seemed to no longer exist. All anyone cared about was the "crazy," and everyone forgot about "Amy." I was desperate. I wanted to leave town, to get away from everyone. I wanted to start somewhere new, where no one knew I had been in the hospital. I thought if my friends really knew who I was, if they really knew the thoughts I had, then they would certainly have run for the hills.

Life at home continued to be difficult and I withdrew further and further. Fights with my parents escalated. I left cabinet doors open or forgot to turn off the lights when I left a room. I couldn't explain that I didn't even remember opening the cabinet door or being in the room. I simply didn't have the words to explain myself. By the time I got home from school, I had little left.

The amount of energy it took for me to get through each day was tremendous. I was short-tempered and forgot things. I was regarded as being obstinate and disrespectful, when in fact I was just tired and medicated. I'm not saying I'm a saint and that there weren't times when I was truly disrespectful. The greatest issues were a result of my inability to talk about things that were bothering me or answer for myself when questioned. If a conversation became just a bit heated, it was as if my whole mind would shut down and I would go into survival mode. This severely impacted my personal relationships in ways I could not begin to understand.

4

After high school, I applied and was accepted to the school furthest from where I lived—Texas Tech University in Lubbock, Texas. Only one person who knew about me would be attending Tech. When the acceptance letter arrived, I felt like I had something to look forward to now. I would be leaving for Lubbock soon. *A new start; a new beginning!*

When I went to college, I tried to be like everyone else, but I still saw myself as mentally ill. *Damaged goods.* Thoughts like *what if they find out... if they only knew who I really was...*constantly ran through my head. It didn't take long for me to stop taking my medication, stop going to classes, and start drinking from the moment I woke up to the time I passed out at night. I had so little self-esteem and my physical size grew at an astounding rate. It was just an outward manifestation of the angst and pain I was in. I began eating comfort foods like never before.

I would stuff myself until I couldn't feel anything but the pain in my stomach from being so full.

Until this point in my life, I was teetering on a ledge but could still grab a foothold to find my way out. No longer was that possible.

I was slipping further into the hole. The more I ate, the deeper it got. I slowly lost touch with reality. I spent hours each day praying to God to save me from this hell on earth. Much of my time was spent either at the Wesley Foundation or the Baptist Student Union looking for salvation from the torment that I lived in every day. I never could explain or put words to what was happening. I thought I was going mad.

During the spring semester of 1993, I was told that in order to stay in school I would have to see the campus psychiatrist and attend counseling. I was ready to try anything to feel better and to be like others around me. I was not sure that would ever be possible. I was tired. I wanted to die each and every minute of the day.

Once the semester was over, I went to Shades of Hope Treatment Center in Buffalo Gap, Texas. At the treatment center, I was put on a strict diet that consisted of no white flour, no sugar, and no caffeine—and, of course, no alcohol. Carolyn was assigned as my counselor. I was so ready for her to be like everyone else, to discount what I said, to call me a liar. I expected her to believe the negative things that were said about me. She never did that.

I remember how hard the first few days were for me and how afraid I was that I couldn't tolerate the emotions I was feeling, but I made it. In the midst of learning to handle my thoughts and emotions, I learned what it meant to be heard. Carolyn allowed me to show her who I was and share *my* truth. I never forgot how that felt. I was in the program for most of the summer, and eventually transitioned into the halfway house. This allowed me a lot more freedom. It was the first time I had been clean and sober for any length of time, since I was about twelve years old.

Not long after this transition into the halfway house, the desire for the "numbing foods" became stronger than any resolve I had at the time. Little by little, I started adding foods back into my diet. At first, I would chew the food and then spit it out. It didn't take long before I went on an all out binge. The negative thoughts and feelings I had about myself returned quickly and with a vengeance. I was too scared to tell the truth about the binge, and had no idea how everything fell apart so fast. I was surrounded by extremely supportive people who believed in me and were doing everything they could to have me win. However, I believed I was unworthy of their support. For a short time, life looked like it was making a turn for the better. I had started to plan for a future. It was gone in an instant. I felt like such a loser.

I was the one person in this world who would never, ever get better. I had proven it.

I fell right back into the pit of despair like I never left. I went on an even worse binge. I ate loaves of bread, gallon containers of ice cream, fast food hamburgers, pizza, donuts, snack cakes—anything and everything I could get my hands on. I could see only one way out: to kill myself. I wanted the pain to be over once and for all so I took all of my medication at once.

To my dismay, I woke up in ICU. I remember the disappointment and hurt in Carolyn's eyes when she came to visit me. I had no answers to give her. It was after this suicide attempt that I heard for the first time "we cannot handle you." The treatment team said I needed more intensive care. Shades of Hope was not a locked psychiatric facility and they were not equipped to deal with me. In my mind they said, "We give up on you."

5

When the ambulance pulled away from the hospital that day, I was strapped down on a gurney and headed to a locked facility in Dallas, Texas. I spent that three hour drive in silence. I refused to answer the questions of the paramedic who sat in the back of the ambulance with me. I was already lost in my head, lost in my thoughts, and the negative messages were taking over. I was losing any fight that I had left within myself. I was 19 years old and I felt like I had lived a hundred lifetimes. I was tired. I wanted someone to fix me, someone to make it all better. I wanted them to give me a pill so I could be like everyone else. Others my age were out enjoying life—having a life outside of high school—going to work or to college. Yet, here I was, walking out of the back of an ambulance; I was embarking on a journey that I would not wish on my worst enemy. I was entering a special type of college.

I was entering the "College of Horrors."

I was being admitted to an adult psychiatric hospital. The courses offered were: Locked Doors, Seclusion, Restraints, Electro-Convulsive Therapy (ECT), Halfway Houses, Group Apartment Living Programs, Board and Care Homes, Adult Foster Care, and

Psychiatric Medications by the Bucket-Full. Once I made it into the admissions department, "The White House" at Timberlawn Hospital, there were forms to sign and questions to answer. I didn't know the answers about insurance and the other forms placed in front of me.

I had never done this before.

My parents were not with me.

I was alone.

I'm just a kid. I can't do this, kept playing over and over in my head. In reality, I was an adult now and I was terrified. Life, as I knew it, was about to radically change.

I walked with a staff member across "The Campus." It felt like I was walking to my death; in a sense I was. When we reached the door to the psychiatric unit I would be staying in, I knew I was in trouble. This was nothing like the hospital I had been in when I was in high school, with kids my age or a bit younger. I stepped through that door and entered an entirely different world– a world no one should have to experience–the world of being a mental patient on a locked psychiatric unit.

While the unit was nicely decorated and light shone in from the center atrium, a sense of despair and darkness lingered. I looked around and what I saw was what I knew I could expect from my life in a few years: People in their 40's, 50's, 60's—lost, alone, and somehow dead inside. I watched as people shuffled around, lost in their own worlds. This is what I had to look forward to.

I was escorted to my own room, my belongings searched, and my shoe strings taken. I was assigned a staff member to be with me every moment of the day. I wanted to be alone. I wanted the whole world to go away. *I wasn't even allowed to go the bathroom by myself.* Those first few days at the hospital were a blur. All I remember is the fear that pulsed through my veins.

I was given large amounts of anti-psychotic medications which were supposed to "quiet" the voices and hallucinations I was having. The medications were also supposed to stop the flashbacks I was having. I became devoid of any emotion—*good or bad.*

I was told I would never work.
I would never have a family.
I would never return to school.

I was also told I would have to live in some type of supportive housing environment for the rest of my life—all because I had been diagnosed with a mental illness. This was the expectation for people like me. In the space of five minutes everything I knew I was supposed to do or accomplish was taken away.

The process of getting on Social Security Disability began. The day I signed the papers to file for Social Security Disability Income and Supplemental Security Income, another huge piece of my world crumbled in. Not only was I mentally ill, but those in authority said I was "disabled," too. What did that mean? At my young age, I thought people who had *physical* disabilities were disabled; I never considered that there was such a thing as a *mental* disability. Yet, here I was, being told that my mental illness was so bad that I was considered *disabled*. These were the professionals. They knew what they were talking about. Professionals know what's best.

At the age of 19 years young, I was approved for Social Security Disability. All this may as well have been a death sentence. Those expectations put out the little flicker of light that I had left. What did I have to fight for? I gave into the "illness." I got lost within myself; lost in the voices and the hallucinations; lost in the darkness and despair. I lived my life in a medicated haze spending my hours rocking back and forth with drool pooling on my chest. This was what my life had come to. I thought I had reached the bottom. I was 19, in an adult psychiatric unit, with a staff member within arm's length at every moment. Little did I know how far down this journey would take me.

I became a really great mental patient.

6

Life consisted of going in and out of the hospital. Between the inpatient hospital stays, I lived in a step-down type of facility which was operated by the hospital. I was living in North Texas and had only spent a few hours at a time with my family. My social security disability benefit was approved, and I received a small amount of back pay. I wanted to go to South Padre Island, my favorite place on earth, and I wanted to go there with my mom. This would be an opportunity for us to spend some time together.

The island had always been a place of refuge while I was growing up. My family and I spent almost every summer there. No matter how dark life seemed to be, no matter what was happening, everything went away when we drove over the causeway and onto the island. I was looking forward to this time together; I was excited and yet I had a sense of dread, too. *Could I do this? Could I be away from the hospital? What if I started wanting to hurt myself? What if I got anxious? What if? What if? What if?* The voice in my head chattered on and on.

By the time we left for the beach, I had worked myself into a frenzy. My emotions were dulled by the medication, so little emotion was actually expressed. I tried *so hard* to be the daughter I thought my mom wanted me to be; not this "mentally ill defect." I recall very little about that trip.

On the first day, I went out as I always had before, but did not know about the sun sensitivity I now had which was caused by the medications. My skin was so sensitive to the sun that I burned horribly. For the remainder of the trip, I sat at the table and stared blankly out the window. Staring blankly had become constant in my life. My mom had not been around me for long periods of time, so she did not know this was how I spent my days.

I had great difficulty carrying on a conversation and, at times, drool would slip down my chin and onto my shirt leaving a visible puddle. It broke my mom's heart to see me this way. She didn't know who I was and, "just wanted her Amy back." I heard this from her frequently, and wanted to scream, "I'm right here!" But I was trapped by the medication haze I was buried under. No words would come out of my mouth. I was sinking deeper and deeper into the abyss.

The quicksand was winning.

Many of my memories are spotty; it's something I have gotten used to over the years. I often used other people's experiences of me to fill in the blanks. My mom used to tell people that trip was *the worst* trip she had ever been on. That trip was a turning point—one where any hope my mom had for my living some kind of "normal life" disappeared.

When she dropped me back off at the hospital, the sadness in her eyes broke my heart. I could see her slumped over the steering wheel from my window. It seemed like she sat there for hours. She was crying. It wasn't often that I saw her cry. It scared me. I was confused, and felt so very alone as I watched her leave. I began to cry. I cried because I could not be the daughter she wanted me to be. I cried for the disappointment that I saw in her eyes.

My mom started to see me as the illness.

I cried for the life sentence I had received; the one that damned me to live this life of despair. We had always loved going to South Padre Island. Now the one place on earth I could always count on to bring happiness to my life, only brought sorrow. Another part of me died after that trip to South Padre Island.

Incessant thoughts took over: *What did she know? What was she thinking? Why me?* I wanted the thoughts to stop. I wanted everything to stop. I wanted out. I pounded myself in the face until my nose bled. Everything dulled for a while—I was distracted enough from the headache and my throbbing nose to fall into a fitful sleep—no relief even in my sleep.

I had restless legs and night terrors. I dreaded going to sleep. I dreaded sleeping as much as I dreaded waking up every morning. My eyes would barely open before I began to curse God for not taking me in my sleep and putting me out of my misery. If He was such a faithful God, shouldn't He listen? Shouldn't peace be provided? I was living in my own internal hell, seemingly with no way out. Life became much heavier.

Life at Timberlawn was a piece of cake
compared to what was to come.

7

I transitioned into the Apartment Living Program across from the halfway house and was provided an apartment of my own. I was still expected to be involved in the activities at the halfway house, and went through the required motions every day. Even though I had gained a little bit of freedom, I cursed each day I was alive. I was a "compliant" program participant. For months, I had been living in the hospital or in the fully staffed halfway house. I was constantly told what to do, when and how to do it. I no longer had staff telling me to make my bed or clean up my area. I was alone for hours with only the thoughts in my head. I had never lived by myself. Now, in the blink of an eye, I had to make decisions for myself. This was something I was not prepared for. I had my "allowance" that I would get from the cashier, and ordered pizza or breadsticks until my money ran out.

One of the requirements for living in the apartment was that I volunteer at the nursing home across the street. At a meeting with my caseworker, I was told to go to the nursing home, introduce myself to the activities director and ask about volunteering. I couldn't say I was afraid to go there alone. I couldn't find the words to express the terror that was growing inside me. *I couldn't breathe.* I was panic stricken. This happened every time I was supposed to talk to someone I didn't know—it felt like there was a vise grip around my chest. It didn't matter if it was supposed to talk to them on the phone or meet them in person.

Over and over, I would scream to myself,
"People your age are supposed to be able to do this!"

I went back to my apartment and cried and cried. I held the phone number I was supposed to call until the ink bled from holding onto the paper so tightly. I felt like I was holding on for dear life. I sat in a dark corner of my room rocking back and forth, staring at the phone. I knew the Activities Director was expecting my call and as I sat there and I begged myself for the courage to take this "simple step." I fought the urge to throw up.

I picked up the phone and made the call. When the Activities Director answered, I hung up on her. This was not anything new for me; I often panicked and hung up when I made phone calls. Thankfully, this was before caller ID. My caseworker called and asked when my appointment was. I lied and told her the lady wasn't in and I was about to call her back. I lied frequently when I couldn't get the words out of my mouth fast enough to tell someone what was going on.

After hours of telling myself I could do it, I made the call. We set an appointment to meet the next day. Anxiously, I walked across the street to meet that lady. Because of my constant medicated state, I remember little about the meeting. I do remember shaking so hard, I thought I might shake right out of the chair. We agreed that I would volunteer a couple times a week. I walked back to my apartment and promptly threw up. How was I going to do this? It hurt to be out in the world—it physically hurt. I couldn't see how I was going be able to do this. That night, I attempted suicide again.

8

I ended up in the inpatient unit again. I had already been hospitalized many times and was taking large doses of psychiatric medications, but nothing was working the way they thought it should. The doctors deemed me "medication resistant." This time they decided to try something different. They met with my parents about giving me electro-convulsive therapy (ECT). I had to sign some forms so I could begin a regimen of ECT.

I was willing to try anything to make it all stop—the headaches, the body aches, the crying, the shaking, the anxiety, the despair—it was unbearable for me. I just wanted to be like my friends. I wanted to live the life I told people I was living. Only my close friends knew the real truth—that I was locked up in an institution. Everyone else was told of adventures I was having, like a life filled with travel and romantic relationships—little did they know, I was sitting in a locked psychiatric unit, rocking back and forth waiting to have electrodes placed on my head and an electrical current jolted through my body.

All this was an attempt "to make me normal." I prayed this "therapy" would be the miracle cure; the thing that would reset my brain, so I could go on and enjoy life. The ECT treatments **were not** the cure that I hoped for, but they provided some relief. The darkness lifted a little bit and after a while in the hospital's half-way house, I was moved to another half-way house program that was to be long-term.

9

Herrin House was located in the crime-riddled heart of East Dallas. We were not allowed to walk anywhere after dark because it was too dangerous. Still, it was considered to be one of the best programs of its kind in our area. I did okay for a while but, as usual, old patterns of anxiety and panic began to emerge. Horrific memories bubbled to the surface of my mind and I had no ability to push them back down.

Anti-psychotic medication didn't make the flashbacks go away.

I started getting food outside the facility. I ordered almost every night from this little pizza place down the road. Two of us would go in together and buy a Stromboli for two dollars each. After eating, the anxiety inside my body would subside for a few minutes, but I couldn't get enough to *numb out*. I felt like I was constantly bumping up against a wall—a wall that seemed impossible for me to get through. I was desperate and wanted relief.

I spotted a razor that was in my room. I had no idea how to pop it open, but found a way. Without another thought, I began to cut my wrist; I cut it deep. Then something happened that altered everything—I could breathe. *I actually felt relief.* The desire to die disappeared. At that very moment, I knew I had discovered a new way of living in my own skin. I dropped the blade and put pressure on the wound. I was taken back to the hospital.

After a short stay, I was released and I was *really* terrified—terrified that I felt so much relief the day I cut my wrist. I had a desire to feel that relief again—and it was a very strong desire. I began to cut different parts of my body and landed in the ER *again and again.* When questioned by the nurses, I was able to explain it all away—I fell on a piece of glass, etc. I was met with suspicious looks, but it was another month or so before a nurse confronted me. I was caught. My secret was out.

I was given a new diagnosis, one that held an even darker stigma than depression or addiction. I was labeled as a "self-abuser." Because of the number of suicide attempts I had on record, as well as my self-abusive behavior, living placements became harder and harder to find. Sometimes, I would sleep on friend's couches until something would happen and I would be asked to leave. I spent many nights on the street in Dallas sleeping in my car. When I had no car, I slept hidden behind bushes. I hid most of this from my family.

I was so ashamed of where life had taken me.

10

Many attempts were made to turn my life around. Once, after I was kicked out of a half-way house placement, I went back to the hospital and they created a special program for me. I was allowed to attend the day hospital program during the day, and I stayed on the inpatient unit at night. I had a long-term hospitalization in a private facility which lasted over three months. I received some of the best therapies offered at the time, yet nothing seemed to work for long. I remember a social worker sitting me down and telling me that she could not find a placement that would accept me because of "my behaviors." I wanted to scream at her. Did she really think I wanted to live like this? Did she really think I wanted all the scars up and down my legs?

I went back to Nacogdoches. I stayed at the apartment of a friend from church camp, because I was not allowed to go home. It was the time of "tough love," and my parents were at the end of their rope. More than once, my mom told me she did not recognize me or know who I had become. *I didn't recognize me.* I was trapped and didn't know how to get out. I took an overdose and, at some point, called my mom. She sent an ambulance to pick me up.

The only person who came to see me was a sheriff. He was there to transport me to the *public* psychiatric hospital. The sheriff ordered me to get out of the bed. He handcuffed me and walked me to the car. Walking to his car was one of the longest walks of my life. I was not an anonymous face in a city of millions of people. I was being treated like a criminal. I was in my hometown.

Life hit a new low.

11

I spent a few days at the psychiatric unit in Lufkin. For the second time, my friend, Angela, came to see me in a psychiatric hospital. She was the only friend who had visited me when I was hospitalized in high school. I felt so embarrassed. She never saw me as a sick person; she always saw me as *Amy*. I wanted desperately to be the person she saw, but I had no idea how to find *that Amy*.

I was transferred back to the private hospital in Nacogdoches. The doctors and nurses didn't know what to do for me. I agreed to go back to the hospital in Dallas for another round of ECT's. This would be my second series in two years. I was willing to do anything for some relief. It felt like my last chance. Once again, I was taken to the "White House" and admitted. I was then escorted to the adult unit. I could walk that path in my sleep.

I was becoming a professional mental patient.

I went through the second round of ECT's. I did a bit better after this round of ECT treatments. I was on less medications and my emotional affect had improved. As my discharge date neared, I could tell that something was different. There was no mention of my going back to some of the "nicer" places I had been. I had private insurance as well as Medicaid and Medicare so that wasn't the issue. The placements I had been in before were unwilling to accept me into their programs again. *The issue was me.* My social worker was getting increasingly frustrated with her inability to find me a placement.

My social worker finally found an apartment living program located in South Oak Cliff, Dallas. I would be living with someone I didn't know, but I would have my own room. I vividly remember driving up to this placement—it was as if I had entered an entirely different universe. I was terrified. I was terrified by the houses that surrounded the complex, by the looks I was given from the people who lived there, and terrified by the condition of the apartment. The caseworker constantly reminded me of how grateful I should be to be able to move into this placement.

I walked in the front door and met my roommate. It was as if she looked straight through me. I scanned the room. I saw a tattered couch with roaches crawling on the walls—nothing else. I was shown to my room. On the floor was a twin mattress, with sheets placed on top—nothing else. In the kitchen, there were a few dirty dishes and one pot—nothing else. The rules were explained. I was told that if we wanted a phone we would need to have one installed. There was a payphone on the street corner. I was advised not to go there after dark. The caseworker left. I was speechless.

Debutante to skid row in a few short years.

Life of my dreams.

98

I stood there, dumbfounded. I was terrified beyond description and didn't know what I was going to do. How was I supposed to get to my appointments? How was I supposed to get groceries? What was I supposed to do all day long? Being grateful for this roof over my head was impossible. I went to my room, made my bed and crawled under the covers. It wasn't long before I heard gunshots. I screamed and burst into tears. I begged God to take me— to let me die. I didn't care if I went to Hell. It couldn't be any worse than the life I was living now.

I went outside to the street corner; the police were everywhere. I prayed for someone to shoot me and put me out of my misery. No one did. There was no overriding the thoughts in my head. It was as if my thoughts had a life of their own. There were not enough ramen noodles or boxes of macaroni and cheese to *numb out* my feelings.

I filled pages and pages of journals, attempting to release the words that continuously repeated in my head. I had all the tools I learned in the hospital. I had been through months of cognitive therapy. None of it worked. The only thing that "worked" for me was cutting—and I did, which sent me straight to the ER. After being sewn up, I was sent to the psychiatric unit where I waited to return to Timberlawn. The South Oak Cliff placement lasted a whopping three weeks.

12

My stay at Timberlawn was short. I was taken to mental health court, diagnosed as both "medication and treatment resistant." I was court committed to the Terrell State Hospital. I was then immediately placed on a van and transported to Terrell, Texas. I had been warned about the "dreaded" State Hospital. I was told many horror stories about it by other patients—*and now I was going there.*

The room I was given was not private and did not have a bathroom. I shared a room with four or five other people. The toilets and showers were down the hall, dormitory-style. I had a panic attack every time I took a shower. I took my clothes into the shower stall with me and came out half wet. Mental illness had landed me here. The place they *had* to accept you. I was in the psychiatric hospital of last resort.

Everything was different in this hospital. There were new rules for me to follow. I couldn't think fast enough to take it all in. I was terrified—normal for me now. I didn't see my doctor or social worker every day. I was assigned a "one-on-one" staff member. The patients in this hospital were hallucinating, throwing chairs, and doing all sorts of unimaginable things. I sat in the corner quietly.

I managed to get out of the State Hospital quickly the first time. The staff and doctors didn't know my history. I told them what they wanted to hear and, within three weeks was discharged. I was done. I was tired. I wanted out—not just out of the hospital, but out of life. I listened to the problems the poor caseworker had finding a placement for me. She finally found someone who would accept me in East Dallas. It was a "board and care home." I had no idea what a "board and care home" was. The "friends" I made in the hospital told me terrifying stories about the "home" I was about to live in. Naively, I thought it couldn't be much worse than the South Oak Cliff placement.

Little did I know how much worse life could get.

A transport driver drove me from the hospital to a dilapidated house with about ten people sitting on couches out front. As I walked in, I almost choked on the stench of body odor. I wanted to run back to the car and beg the driver to take me anywhere other than where he was leaving me. Instead, I walked numbly behind the house manager into the house. I was introduced to the staff through burglar bars that separated them from us. I was escorted upstairs to my room. There was nowhere for me to put my things. It didn't matter—most of my clothes and possessions had been lost or stolen through my many hospitalizations and placements.

I did have a little purple box that held my most precious belongings, which I hid under my mattress. Through all the hospitalizations, all the living placements, and even sleeping behind the bushes, I had that box with me. The box held a little wooden pendant cross, a few pictures, some handwritten affirmations from a church friend, a bible verse card from Angela, one marble from Shades of Hope, a book and a tiny clay inner child statue that Carolyn had given me. The book was, "*The Greatest Miracle in the World*," by Og Mandino. I never understood my deep need to keep that book, yet it was always there.

The "home" was to be the recipient of my disability income. The house manager was responsible for providing me with food and transportation to my appointments. We were fed peanut butter and jelly sandwiches every day. On Fridays, we had Cici's pizza. The residents were treated horribly by the staff. There were no activities. I sat alone, for hours on end, trapped with the incessant thoughts in my mind. I was miserable. My mother did come to visit a couple of times, but said it was too hard for her to see me living like that and know she had to leave me there.

I felt abandoned—completely alone.

Again, I resorted to cutting—it brought some sense of relief, even if it was only for a few minutes. Of course, I landed back in Terrell State Hospital. This time I stayed longer than the first time. As discharge neared, I was terrified of being sent back to the "home." I tried over and over to tell my treatment team why I didn't want to go back. It was as if I was paralyzed—the words simply would not come out of my mouth. I *knew* if I told them the truth they wouldn't believe me. It was *actually safer* in the "dreaded" State Hospital than the "home."

I found a way to cut *in the hospital*. Despite that, I was discharged within a day. This began a cycle of self-harm, hospitalization, discharge, and boarding homes. I was sent to a "day hospital" across town from the "home." The doctor at the day hospital increased my medication and provided me with a full month's supply. On my way out, I stepped into the bathroom and swallowed a bottle and a half of pills. I got onto the transport van like nothing happened. I knew how long it would take us to get across town, and if I could make it to my room without being noticed I could go to sleep. That would be it, I would finally be free: free from the prison I lived in, free from constant torment, free from despair. I would be free.

13

I woke up several days later in ICU, alive and mad as hell. I couldn't even kill myself. I was furious that I was still alive. The nurse caring for me got right up in my face, made me look her in the eye, and told me there was a reason I was still alive. I never forgot her. She was kind to me—good to me—even though I was spewing anger at her. This interaction started a shift in the direction my life had been going. My clothes were lost in the ER. I was transferred *back* to Timberlawn wearing *nothing but a hospital gown and a blanket.*

I spent an entire week in a private psychiatric hospital wearing that same hospital gown and blanket.

I was transported once again to Terrell State Hospital wearing nothing but *that same* hospital gown and a straight jacket. When I arrived at Terrell and was unstrapped from the jacket, one of the staff members said, "Oh no, no, no! This is not ok! Let's get her something to wear." Within five minutes I had a bra, underwear and clothes to put on. I cried. I cried because I was *so* embarrassed that I had been virtually naked for *over a week.* I cried because someone finally *showed me some compassion.* This was at the end of August, 1996. I was beginning what would be my longest *and last* hospital stay. At this point, I had been hospitalized somewhere between 40 and 50 times. I was 23 years old.

I met with the doctor the next day and she gave me a choice. She said I could be discharged and I'd probably be dead in a week, or I could stay. She said that I could get better. She also said that working on recovery would be the hardest thing I had ever done. I had been told many things that I "could not" do. The only thing I had been told I "could" do was take my medication, and take it on time. Now I was sitting in front of a DOCTOR who was telling me I COULD GET BETTER!

No one had ever said I could get better.

On that day, I took a leap of faith. I started a new journey. I had a true desire to have a life that didn't hurt. I was given time to work on my trauma issues. Once again, I was working with someone who was on my side, who heard me, who allowed me to share and work through what happened to me. The staff supported me like the staff at Shades of Hope had. They acknowledged the pain I felt. They asked me what I thought I could do instead of hurting myself when I felt overwhelmed. They stopped focusing on my self-abusive behavior, which allowed me to let go of the shame I felt about it all. I felt safe again. I began to feel like a *human being* again for the first time since I was 16 years old.

The most amazing thing happened: I got a client worker job and was paid. This was unbelievable to me! I had been told I would never work, yet here I was going to work every day. On the weekends I took care of the garden. I had a purpose. I had something to look forward to each day. The first day at my client worker job I started crying when I was asked to separate some plants and repot them. I knew I was going to kill those plants. Three weeks later, the staff called me to the back of the greenhouse to show me the plants—all were alive and growing. I cried because I hadn't killed them!

I thought I was such a bad person, and was certain that anyone or anything that came in contact with me would be harmed. This perception I had of myself began to shift. I started believing that maybe—just maybe—I wasn't as broken or bad as I thought. One day I was asked about my hopes and dreams.

I never thought I'd live past my mid 20's,
much less live outside an institution.

I couldn't answer the question. I was encouraged to start dreaming and to focus on what I wanted to do with my life. I got very frustrated because I did not know what I liked, what I wanted, or what was possible. Eventually, I made a "Dreams List." I wrote things that seemed extremely hard for me to accomplish. I wanted to be a productive citizen. I wanted live on my own. I wanted to have a family. I wanted to do some fun things like put my toes in the Pacific Ocean, go to Washington DC, and snorkel in Hawaii.

14

On August 1, 1997, I was discharged from Terrell State Hospital, and moved into an efficiency apartment. I had been hospitalized for almost a year. I hadn't been able to stay out of the hospital in the past, but the staff believed I could this time. I held on to their faith. They had faith that I could make it.

For the most part life was okay. I was vigilant in hiding my mental illness—I did what I was told, went to my appointments and took my medications on time. Life looked so much better than it had before, yet being out in the world was a constant struggle for me. The people in my life were proud of how far I'd come, yet also knew how hard it was for me to simply make it through the day. I slept a lot. My anxiety was through the roof. I tried to hide everything, but there were times when I would lash out or collapse into tears. I rarely went out. I would leave events early or not go at all.

My behavior was tolerated because, after all,
I was mentally ill.

Within three years, I began working part-time at the state hospital—the same state hospital I had been discharged from. I worked on the weekends—10 hours a day in the family center. My job was greeting families and setting up visits.   The job was hard for me. Every day I was worried about whether I would be able to show up for my next shift.   I was in contact with many more people than I ever had been before. The work pushed me to the edge of my capacity.

I was good at wearing a smile on my face. After working for 20 hours on the weekend, it took me days to recover. I *had to* spend as much time as I could sitting still and being quiet. Chores didn't get done. It looked like I was lazy. I felt like I was lazy. My family and I would talk about why I acted one way in public, yet when I got home I was a completely different person. I didn't understand it—it was the only way I could cope.

No one understood the energy it took from me to get through a day. I couldn't explain what I had to do to be in the world. They tried to understand, but never did. I knew they loved me and cared about me—yet they watched me like a hawk for any signs of relapse. They would have been terrified if they knew how much I was really struggling.

I was holding on by the skin of my teeth.

In time, I learned to deal with the "symptoms" of my illness and pretend to be happy. I accepted a full-time position at Terrell State Hospital, in 2001. I willed myself forward every day. I told myself that I should be grateful for the life I had; that I should be grateful *to be the one holding the keys* and not the one being locked up anymore. Life was getting very busy for me. I began to transition off disability. There were many times I just wanted the world to stop. I was tired and I couldn't tell anyone what I was thinking.

In September of 2001, my mom was diagnosed with late stage cancer. It felt like my world was crashing in. While we had a strained relationship at times, she had always been there for me. Now things had to be done for her—*I had to step up.* I didn't want her to worry about me. I turned to food with a vengeance. I ate everything that comforted me. I drove to fast food places any time I could sneak out of the house. I wanted to be numb. I had just begun this full-time job and now my mom was very sick. I was being asked to do things that terrified me. My mom needed me to make phone calls for her— the thought of calling people I didn't know, once again, sent me into a panic.

My personal relationships started to suffer. It took everything I had to perform the basic tasks of each day. I turned inward hoping to preserve the little bit of sanity I thought I had. After a two and a half year battle with cancer, my mother passed away in May of 2004. I learned more from her in those years than I had in my whole life. I promised her I would be okay. I had no idea how I would keep that promise. The weight of that promise was crushing at times.

For years to come, my mom's illness and death would replay in my head like a movie. It was maddening. Memories would play over and over again. It was as though I was on a ride and there was no getting off. No amount of self-talk or psychotherapy could get me past those memories.

My personal relationships suffered even more. My work life was getting busier—requiring more of my energy. I couldn't do both; I didn't have it in me to do both. All I could do was put one foot in front of the other. I felt as though something had to change. I moved out of the house I had been living in for 9 years. I was now out on my own.

15

Taking that part-time job at Terrell State Hospital turned out to be one of the best things that happened in my life. It gave me access to the value of my "lived experience of mental illness." It was valuable because I could share my experiences with others. Over the next several years, I was given new responsibilities at work. I began speaking to new employees and nursing students about how to interact with patients. I spoke of the treatment I had received—the good and the horrible. I taught them how critical it is to treat people with dignity and respect.

Respectful treatment can be the difference between life and death.

In 2007, I was trained as a Peer Support Specialist and returned home to help form the first Peer Support Organization for the State Hospital System in Texas. I also began serving on several statewide committees, which meant I began to travel. A number of my weekends were now filled with more people and more demands. I didn't know if I could keep up the pace. Life from the outside looked okay, but all I thought was, *"if they only knew."*

In August of 2010, I was asked to be a Keynote Speaker at the Lake's Regional MHMR Empowerment Banquet in Greenville, Texas. I had spoken in front of large audiences before, but I had never been a Keynote Speaker. I was looking for inspiration for my speech and picked up the book, *The Greatest Miracle in the World.*

I suddenly wanted to find Carolyn. I wanted to tell her I was still alive and that my life was really great (I was always trying to convince myself of this). I also wanted to thank her for the impact she had on my life and to apologize for the way I left years before. I had tried to find her before, but never could.

A few weeks after I gave the speech, Carolyn was still on my mind so I started searching for her name on Google. Much to my surprise, she was there. I sent her a message that day, not knowing if she would even remember me—it had been over 18 years since our paths had crossed. I watched my e-mails hoping for a response. A few days later there it was. Not only did she remember me, but we had colleagues in common.

Life went on as usual that fall, yet I felt like I was walking around with concrete boots. Since e-mailing with Carolyn, I had been thinking about my time at Shades of Hope Treatment Center. I remembered that I felt better, physically and emotionally, when I had been at Shades. I wanted to go back on their food program, but really believed I needed comfort foods in order to survive.

In December of 2010, now working as a Peer Support Specialist Supervisor, I was assisting a patient to set reasonable, achievable health goals. I knew I could not encourage someone else to do something that I couldn't do myself, so I started by setting my own goal: limiting sugar sodas. I had not been willing to take a serious look at this area of my life up until this point. I had eliminated all kinds of self-abusive behaviors, yet the thought of dealing with the foods I ate made me want to run for the hills. At least limiting sodas was a start.

16

In February of 2011, I received a call at lunch. I didn't recognize the number so I let it go to voicemail. The voice on that message was one I recognized instantly, but had not heard in over 18 years—*it was Carolyn and she wanted me to call her back.*

I returned her call quickly. It felt like no time had passed. I was able to thank her for the help she had given me. I was finally able to tell her the things I had wanted to say for so long. I remembered how much I trusted her. I told her about the trials and triumphs of my life. I told her about my work, about the committees I was on, and about the places I was speaking around Texas. I also told her how I was feeling that day—I was having a really hard time.

My friend committed suicide the night before, while I was on the phone with him. It was a surreal experience to be speaking with Carolyn for the first time in almost 20 years. The last time I saw her, *I was the one who had attempted suicide.*

The next time we spoke, I told Carolyn where my journey had taken me. I talked about some of the problems I was having with my medications. I told her I was slowly coming off them. Because of the lowered doses in my medication, I was struggling mentally and emotionally. I was not sleeping much. My anxiety had increased. Words were harder and harder to get out of my mouth. I didn't tell her that according to my lab results, my body was toxic. My liver and kidney function was damaged from nearly 24 years of heavy doses of psychiatric medications. I only told her that my doctor and I were slowly decreasing the dosage on each medication.

I was too scared to tell Carolyn—or my doctor—the terror I felt about reducing my medications. Surviving my life day-to-day took more than anyone knew. I desperately wanted life to stop being so hard—to stop being such a struggle. I was tired of going to work and then having to spend the whole night sitting in my recliner, staring at the wall, so I could regroup and do it again the next day. I was tired of the life I had. I was desperate to *live*.

I was 36 years old, and this was the best life had to offer me.

I talked with Carolyn about my eating habits. I told her I had been thinking about going back on the "Shades of Hope" food plan. I remembered feeling better on it and thought it might help. I knew something needed to change. After listening to my ideas for a new food plan, Carolyn told me what she had learned about food, and its effect on her.

Carolyn's symptoms were so similar to mine that I found myself listening in an entirely new way. She had been given many physical and psychiatric diagnoses. The horrible anxiety she felt made it difficult for her to leave the house. Because of panic attacks, she

116

frequently left full shopping carts in the grocery store. She told me how hard it had been for her to be around people. Her legs kicked wildly at night. She had eczema and scratched her scalp in her sleep until it bled. She had mouth ulcers and stomach aches and cried at the drop of a hat. She often screamed in her sleep, upsetting both animals and people. All these were symptoms that medications never relieved.

I was surprised by the number of symptoms we had in common. I used bottle after bottle of Icy Hot trying to get a bit of relief at night from my aching, kicking legs. I coated my mouth in Orajel, and had biopsies to find out why I had so many mouth ulcers. I used cortisone cream, Benadryl lotion, calamine lotion—all trying to relieve itching. I was told these issues were hereditary. Carolyn said most of her symptoms went away after her friend, Ronda, told her to stop eating "gluten."

Everything around me went silent.

She said her symptoms *simply disappeared.* How could this be? Could gluten have caused these symptoms in me? Was it possible? What if food was the answer? Was I fooling myself by even asking these questions? I was mentally ill, after all. These "symptoms" had been with me for years and they fit the basic criteria for all my diagnoses.

I knew Carolyn to be trustworthy. She wouldn't be saying this if it weren't true. Did she really say food caused her to stay locked in her room? Did she say FOOD caused her to cry all the time? Food caused her skin to hurt? Food—gluten—did all that? Carolyn told me to try removing gluten for two weeks. I was to start by removing bread, pasta, cookies and cake. She said it was imperative for me to stick with it for two full weeks. NO CHEATING!

I was willing to see what happened. I only had to eat this way for two weeks—nothing more. If removing gluten meant freedom, I had to try. It certainly couldn't hurt. I could last two weeks on her plan. I had done harder things. In the course of one very long phone call, I became willing to give up the foods I thought I had to have in order to survive life at all.

For the first time since I was twelve, I had hope.

17

When we finally got off the phone, my mind was racing. I replayed every minute of the conversation. What the heck was gluten, anyway? I Googled gluten and was instantly overwhelmed. **Gluten is in almost everything.** I kept reminding myself that she said "Start with removing bread, pasta, cookies, and cake." I tried to wrap my head around the idea of *NOT* eating those foods. Nearly everything I ate fit into one of those four categories—those were *my* four food groups. What was I going to eat?

Carolyn was adamant that I prepare myself for eating gluten free. I was told to make a menu and purchase what I would need for the week. I needed to have gluten free snacks on hand at all times. I was supposed to cook several meals and freeze them so I would always have food ready to eat. Several weeks passed before I was ready to take this step. I planned to start on a Monday. The weekend before I was to start, I ate as much bread, pasta, cookies, and cake as I could. I made myself absolutely sick.

The first few days of eating gluten free were excruciating for me. My anxiety went through the roof. My mind was reeling and my body ached all over. I craved my usual comfort foods—the ones I couldn't eat. Carolyn's words repeated over and over in my head, "The symptoms went away. They simply disappeared. It all went away." I wanted that more than anything in the world. I was determined to make it through the two weeks.

I had to know if this would help.

I relied on the coping skills I had been taught at the hospital. I took lots of hot baths. I had many phone calls with Carolyn. I wrote in my journal. I began taking walks around the block. Overall, things were going well.

Within a few short weeks, I was no longer craving bread or pasta every minute of the day. I was starting to lose weight; it was simply disappearing. It was so strange to me. I had more energy; my thoughts were becoming clear. I found it much easier to say what I wanted to say. I planted a garden in my back yard. I worked on it at night and on the weekends. All this was happening, and I wasn't even thinking about it.

One night, after a particularly long day at work, I came home, changed my clothes, and headed straight out to work in the yard. I got half way out the door and stopped. I thought, "I feel good." It was a surreal moment. The only thing that had changed was what I was eating. I chose to continue eating gluten free because I felt good.

My mind and body felt good!

18

By May, life continued to get easier and easier. I was thinking differently. I was acting differently. I had more energy. I was sleeping better. The world felt brighter to me. My feelings were changing. I was interacting with life in a whole new way. I barely recognized myself.

The anniversary of my mom's death came and went without difficulty. I was shocked. In the eight years since her death, I had to take off work and be heavily medicated to make it through that day. In the past, I was so overcome with grief that my doctor would give me what I called "the bomb"—it was a mix of several anti-psychotics and sedatives. This year was dramatically different. The sadness didn't consume every minute of my life like it had all the years before. I did feel some angst as the date approached, but I didn't feel devastated. I didn't even feel *significantly* sad. I just felt sad—plain old sad.

It was not a problem for me to stay away from bread, pasta, cookies, and cake. Through my conversations with Carolyn, I was learning about *everything gluten was in*—canned goods, spices, toothpaste, shampoo, etc... I knew I was still ingesting gluten, but I felt so much better.

Near the end of May, after work one night, I was really tired and not thinking. I went to get gas and picked up some cheese bread from the local pizza place. I went home, ate and went to bed. By the next night talking was difficult. I was on the phone with Carolyn. My words no longer flowed freely. I was cursing and apologizing profusely for everything I said. She asked what I had eaten because she noticed the dramatic difference. My whole world was rocked that night. The following is an excerpt from an e-mail I sent her:

5/26/2011 I don't know why I am bothering you this morning again except I've got to get what's running in my head out and not just on paper to myself because I cannot see clearly to validate or invalidate what's going on so it keeps spinning. As I settled down to go to sleep last night, my feet and legs were twitching, itching, my body ached, and my legs kicked all night long. My eyelids feel as if they are sunburned, my skin is crawling, and in a sense there is a numb feeling in my body too. I've been short with people, kind of barking at times. I cried in the bathroom at work because I didn't know what was going on. So with all that being said, all I did was eat cheese bread. That's all.

So here is the question, am I making all this up? Am I making up the fact that when I look back over the last few months when I have been off bread and pasta that I have not been a circle talker, that my interactions with others have been concise for the most part—that I have been talking in "normal conversation?" My body has not ached the way it does today and has not felt this heavy. I don't know what the hell I am talking about. I'm sitting here trying to make sense or put meaning to an achy stomach, itchy skin, angst, circle talking, grouchiness, all the things I've lived with my whole life. Am I just taking the words you were saying over the last few months and putting meaning to them?

I don't know why after getting gasoline two days ago, I just called and ordered the cheese bread as though I have not been keeping bread out of my diet. Here's the deal: I'm squirrely this morning, and I know it. So what is the purpose of me writing this and sending it except I need to, ugh! So here's what I am not saying: there are many experiences that we have had in our lives that are similar and it's a bit freaky at times. As you have shared about the food issues, I've always "gotten" it—like I can really understand what you are saying. I don't want to be having some psychosomatic reaction to eating flour. I don't want to say that I feel like I am falling back in the hole when all I did was eat some bread.

I'm still not sure how you knew I ate flour, and quite a bit of it, and thank you for saying it. I do not know if I would have put all of this together, my head is too fuzzy. I had attributed the anxiety and all that's going on to a talk I am giving tomorrow, even though it is a talk that I can do in my sleep. The talk was the only thing I could map the *emotional responses onto; and the achiness, the tiredness, I mapped it onto the weather. Not food!*

19

The new life I was starting to count on slipped away in an instant and I was back to holding on by the skin of my teeth. The emotional responses I was having sent my head reeling. My self-questioning was exhausting: Was I getting sick? Was I coming off my medication too fast? Was I headed for a crash? What if it isn't really food? How does she really know?

Thankfully, I had Carolyn to talk me through it. She reminded me it was just food and not an emotional breakdown. She said I would feel better in a few days if I didn't eat any more gluten. In less than a week, I felt better again. No medications were added; no intense therapy occurred. I didn't take the week off work so I could recover. I trudged through the days, step by step, and soon was right back to where I had been before I put that cheese bread in my mouth. Carolyn heard it; she didn't see me eat it. I didn't tell her I ate it; she heard me talking and instantly knew I was having a reaction to gluten. My, what big ears she has!

That experience provided me a whole new level of understanding about the impact gluten has had, not only on my emotional health, but my physical health as well. No longer could I bury my head in the sand. *I knew*...I saw firsthand the impact gluten had on my emotions and my physical body as a result of eating that cheese bread.

Any questions I had about the changes I was seeing in myself were no longer questions. That incident convinced me that the freedom I was now experiencing in my life was directly linked to the food I was eating. I was now willing to take the next step and go entirely gluten free. Going gluten free seemed daunting; gluten is in almost everything. I was scared.

Carolyn and I talked at length about all the foods that contained gluten. I started doing my own research, looking at many different websites trying to understand the word "gluten." I set July 1, 2011, as the day I would go fully gluten free. I had a month to prepare—to get ready—and I needed it. This journey would challenge who I had known myself to be, and everything I thought about my life.

During this preparation month, Carolyn and I started to examine the new found freedom I was having in my thoughts, in my movement, and in my ability to simply be around people. I was trying to wrap my head around the changes that were occurring for me physically and emotionally. The changes seemed subtle to me, but they were starting to be noticed by my co-workers and friends. I began receiving compliments about how good I looked, and about the weight I had lost. I still hadn't told anyone what I was doing.

I took a vacation and went to Carolyn's house for a week. I learned how to read labels. I learned how to cook new dishes, and fix "funny" foods—like, vegetables! Each morning we would get up and walk two miles with her friends. It took everything I had to keep up with the group. I huffed and puffed, but I was doing it! It was a huge accomplishment for me.

On Thursday, as we took our morning walk, I felt/heard a pop in my head and everything stood still. The world became bright. The sound of the birds became clear. I wanted to talk....*really talk*. My words were ready to flow. I had been fully gluten free for almost two weeks. A fog was lifting, sloughing off, day after day. We went back to the house, sat down, and I started talking. I talked, and talked, and talked. I was sharing my thoughts and feelings without effort.

The words that previously took so much energy to formulate were easily flowing. When it was time for Carolyn to go to yoga, she said she didn't want to go since I was talking so freely. I said, "Go. Don't worry; I'll still be talking when you get back." I was right. When she came back, I picked up right where I left off. That was one of the greatest experiences I have had—it was so liberating. I never knew it could be so easy for me to carry on a conversation.

For the first time in my life, I felt I could really speak.

20

The next morning I woke up, and the first thing I noticed was silence. My head was quiet. There was a sense of peace inside me that I had never known. I had always lived with some kind of anxiety underlying everything. That angst was gone. I had been set free by not eating any gluten. I cried with relief. I felt lighter than I had ever felt in my life. All I had done was take gluten out of my diet. I emailed Carolyn:

7/3/2011 Who I knew myself to be just a few short months ago has changed in every way. I was living a life that was beyond the expectations that had been set for me. However, there had been many limits in all areas of my life. I don't know whether those limits were from within, from the physical weight I carried around, or from the "weight" of the mental illness diagnoses. I do know those limits were real for me. My life was very controlled with little freedom. I have learned over the years that I must constantly be aware of my surroundings, top to bottom, left to right and every centimeter in between. All this was required so I could control my reactions to what was happening around me.

I have lived my life knowing that at any moment things could go to hell in a hand basket. I've always lived with the ever-present fear that I could slip into the hole—slide into a psychosis and never come back. I "knew" that I had a mental illness and it was out of my control. My job was to manage myself to the best of my ability. I spent years taking handfuls of pills. I lived on a strict sleeping schedule. I had to control my evenings and make sure they were filled with lots of down time just so I could make it through each week without overdoing it. I did this successfully for the most part.

I consistently proclaimed that I was grateful to have the life I had achieved. The truth is that I lived in an almost continual state of anxiety. I constantly scanned my environment so I would know who and what was around me. I relied on what I knew about others and their reactions in order to determine where I stood with them each day. I took many things personally. I was always apologizing, almost as if I was apologizing for taking up space in the world.

While I had most certainly come a long way from the years when I was hospitalized, I still saw myself through the lens of a mentally ill person. The things I was told about never being able to work, that I would always have to be taken care of, that I could not return to school, that I would have to manage a life long illness, and that I would always be disabled, reverberated in the back of my head as a constant reminder of who I was and the place I held in this world.

No matter what meeting I was in or what speech I was giving, I always had a reminder of my place in life. I knew I must never forget.

That mentally ill view I had of myself also gave me an excuse—an excuse to sit around and watch TV. I had to have down time, and I certainly could not manage my weight. After all, it's impossible to lose weight on all the medications—or so I told myself. I would allow things to fly out of my mouth and blame the medication. I could not manage my finances or household at times, all the while putting the blame on this serious and persistent mental illness that attacked my brain at such a young age.

I saw myself with limitations; I had internal chains and blinders firmly in place that kept me from seeing what was possible for my life. There were many people that agreed with those limitations. Over the years the chains lengthened and instead of being confined in a 6x6 seclusion room, I now had free range to walk around the "house." It was kind of comfortable, and much better than sleeping on a concrete floor. The windows in my "house" were frosted over and while sunlight shown through, I was still never able to fully see what was beyond the filtered light. I've had periods in my life where I wondered what was on the other side of the frosted glass, yet such thoughts faded fast. The chains were too strong, and the blinders too debilitating.

After a few weeks without the bread and pasta, it was as though the frosted glass started to clear. For the first time in my life I really got to see what was on the other side. At first, the peep-hole was just the size of a quarter—life was out there, a life beyond anything I ever *thought possible. I saw pure sunshine and it was beautiful. Life started changing by leaps and bounds. The clearing in the window was now the size of a tennis ball and I started to see possibilities for my life that I never thought would exist for me; a life free from the chains that have bound me since I was a little kid.*

I started to see the possibility of being free from the confines of my "safe house." There suddenly is a whole world out there for me to see, explore and experience free from the view through a sick and disabled lens. I can see that freedom; I know it is there. Although I am on day three of being fully gluten free, so much has already shifted. I look forward to using the key that you gave me to set myself free.

After that week at Carolyn's, I drove to Austin. I was to meet with a group of people and attend a council meeting. I hadn't seen any of them since April. Carolyn and I discussed what kinds of reactions I might receive from people regarding how much I had changed. Nothing could have prepared me for what actually happened. I knew I was different, but was not aware of how radically I had changed. I had no anxiety as I entered that restaurant. I met with the staff early to discuss the meeting. I felt light. I was comfortable in my own skin.

When the council members saw me, they kept looking at me as though they were trying to figure out what was different. Many made comments about my weight loss. Someone said I was "Sassy!"

Everyone laughed. I said, "Thank you," and laughed, too—I found the conversation amusing. I wasn't trying to blend in with the crowd anymore. I was the center of attention, and I didn't want to crawl out of my skin. I felt free. It was a great night, the first of many, all because I was no longer eating gluten.

The next day I woke up ready to chair the meeting. I experienced *no anxiety*. When I went into the meeting, my words were there. The meeting went more smoothly than ever before. At lunch, I took a deep breath, reviewed the morning, and was in awe of how effortless it had all been—how easily my words flowed.

I lived with constant anxiety for over 30 years, and it was gone!

21

Later in the summer, I went to Austin for another meeting. I had been fully gluten free for almost a month. When I was driving home I noticed I felt odd and my thoughts were going in circles. I stopped in a parking lot to call Carolyn. She asked me what I had eaten, I told her that I had a salad with some dressing and I scraped the sauce off the meat. She said, "It takes just a little bit of gluten to cause a reaction, and it sounds like you're having one. The gluten was most likely in the dressing or the sauce left on the meat." I was stunned. I read that menu carefully. I ordered things that should have been safe.

I didn't ask if the food was gluten free.

I began to panic. I had been "glutened." We hung up the phone and I drove straight home, holding onto the steering wheel for dear life. For that three hour drive, all I could do was feel the subtle changes occurring in my body. For years I had calluses on my hands from gripping the steering wheel tightly. Every time a car entered the highway, I jumped. My skin began to itch. I was scratching my hands and arms. My body ached and I was uncomfortable.

Anxiety was taking over. I wanted to get home, take a bath, and wash everything off of me. The few conversations I had on the way home were strained. Expressing what I wanted to say was difficult. I found myself repeating my point over and over again, not because the person didn't understand me, because I couldn't shut up.

On that drive, I watched my life
slide back into the "hole."

The next few days were a blur. I felt overwhelming panic. I cried a lot. I stuttered and was unable to formulate sentences well. I wanted out of this world. I wanted to die. I was terrified that I was "losing my mind." Thankfully, I was still listening to Carolyn. She repeatedly told me *it was food and I was not mentally ill.* She reminded me of the "accidental glutening" she had a few months before, which I had witnessed. Even with that as a reminder, the darkness felt like it was closing in on me.

I felt like I was turning back into the person who had to fight for every word, the person who always wanted to jump out of her skin, the person who trudged through each day seeking to somehow, someway, *anyway* make the uncontrollable feelings stop. The incessant thoughts returned: those thoughts that were always in the background telling me how the world would be better without me in it, and that my life was damned to be a constant struggle and fight.

Crazy Amy was back with a vengeance.

My whole body hurt. I felt like I had the flu. Talking to Carolyn exhausted me. The thought of having to put on the "fake face" in order to go into work was too much. I couldn't bear to be around anyone. I called in sick to work that Monday. I wanted out of my body and out of my head. I hid in my house.

About four days after I had eaten the gluten, my body stopped hurting. I wasn't tearing up as easily. I didn't wake up angry. By the end of the week, I was good again—better than good. My thoughts were flowing, I was laughing, and life was great. How was this possible? Was I rapid cycling—bouncing back and forth between mania and depression? No! The allergic-type reaction had run its course. The gluten was out of my system. It was as simple as that.

My mind began to reel—it felt like I had just come out of a storm. Food...food! As I began to wrap my head around this experience, feelings of anger began to stir. For fourteen years I had celebrated the first day of August as being my "re-birth" day. It was the day I was discharged from the hospital for the last time. I was usually excited as I drove through the back gate of the hospital. I would think about how ironic it was that I held the keys now—*it's much better to have the keys*. This year was different. I wasn't excited—I was extremely angry.

8/1/2011 *"...years of seeing myself as mentally ill, sick, broken, damaged, have become a memory of my past. Today, for the most part, I do not see myself as any of those labels, and I must say it feels really* strange. I've had trauma in my life, and that did impact my thought processes, the way I viewed myself, my surroundings, and then there was the damning diagnosis of mental illness. Those diagnoses determined how I've seen myself since I was 12–I am 37 years old.

Today I sit here and those labels do not fit. It is such a weird place to be this morning–a weird head space. It is nearly impossible to try and wrap my head around the fact that the constant despair and angst I lived with for so many years has really been because of the foods I was eating. There is a part of me that just wants to cry and kick and scream, and to lash out at God and the universe for this cruel joke.

I've lived so many years in such a fog, unable to see the true beauty that this life has to offer, because I was told I was mentally ill. I convinced myself that I should be grateful for the life I had because it was so much better than others around me. In fact, it was a bunch of bull and by removing this thing called gluten from my diet a whole new world has opened up. I have to trust in perfect timing and that we all have our journey to take, but I feel angry! I feel angry that I lost so many years of my life; angry that I have had to struggle so hard for each breath I took at times; and all the while it was food..."

I was beginning to see the impact gluten had in my life. People told me I looked great and that I seemed really happy. Many comments were made about the weight I was losing. I knew what was happening, but was still reluctant to tell anyone about my new diet.

How was I going to tell the people I've known for years—doctors, nurses, staff, co-workers, friends, family—everything changed because I removed a particular food from my diet? I wanted to shout from the rooftops, "Well, you see, what's actually happening is that I'm coming alive. I'm not eating gluten and I'm being reborn."

Nothing was the same. I wasn't the same.

22

I was nearing the date my psychiatrist and I had set for me to take my final dose of medication. Almost a year had passed. Soon, I would be taking my last pill. I was on the cusp of something I never thought would be possible. I didn't have a clue how to talk with the people in my life about coming off all of my medications. Could I really be alright without taking any psychiatric medications?

Each week I was gluten free, more and more opened up in my life. I learned to trust myself. I began diverting from the carefully scripted speeches I gave to the nursing students. I began to share my thoughts—not just tell the story and events of my life. I actually shared my feelings and told them things I was never willing to tell. I remember a few times after I finished speaking, I would think to myself, "Did I just say that?" I did, and the world didn't fall apart. I wasn't overcome by panic—I was still standing and I felt really good.

Little by little, I was getting to know myself in a whole new way. I still did not trust that this new found life was here to stay. I frequently wondered if this was some sort of trick and the illness would take over and drag me back into the hole. Day after day it did not happen; I did not fall into the hole.

The day arrived that I was to take my last pill. I wanted to celebrate, but thought I was going to throw up. I was so afraid. I tortured myself with questions all day, *"What if my life falls apart now that I am off the medications, what if,* **what if, WHAT IF?!"**

I was able to talk myself through it, knowing that if I had a need for medication, I could always take it again. I never thought about the fact that I had been reducing the medication for an entire year. What if after all these years, I didn't need it anymore? What if removing gluten really was the answer? I was doing better than I had ever done in my life. That night, I took the last dose of psychiatric medication I was ever going to take, and went to sleep.

23

When I woke up on September 12, 2011, I had a spring in my step. I was celebrating my first day of being medication free. I wanted to shout from the roof tops, but I knew better. Had the people in my life known I was no longer taking medication, I don't think I would have been able to breathe. There were too many people watching me. Everyone in my life was trained to check up on me. Any sign of excitement was considered a warning sign for mania—tears indicated depression. Emotions were treated as symptoms requiring medication. I now knew differently. I decided I would tell people after I had been medication free for an entire year.

I kept my mouth shut about the medication
and enjoyed my new life.

Life continued to change for me, step-by-step, day-by-day. I watched myself go through anniversary dates that had previously caused me intense pain or landed me in the hospital. Those dates came and went with little more than a brief thought. I only thought about the anniversaries when someone would check on me. *I was fine. I was more than fine.*

When I recognized that I was actually free from the painful patterns of my past, I broke down and cried—not from sadness or pain—but with joy and relief. For the first time in my life, I was able to experience pure emotion. I felt sad about what had happened in my past. I felt sad about the time I lost during those years—that was it—I simply felt sad. Years of talking and therapy had only gotten me so far. Removing gluten set me free.

The first person I told about my gluten-free diet was my friend, Angela. She knew me better than anyone else and was about to visit for the weekend. To this day, I remember the look of joy in her eyes when she first saw me. She knew I was okay. I was better than okay. I was great! We talked a lot that weekend about my gluten free diet. She is a nurse and I kept looking for skepticism from her. There was none. She didn't need convincing. She saw the results. She saw the ease in my attitude and the light in my eyes.

That weekend we cleaned out my closet and filled four or five large trash bags with clothes that were too big for me. The largest sizes I had in my closest were a 30/32, and size 5X. We were playing around and both got into a pair of sweat pants I had worn the winter before: Angela stood in one leg and I stood in the other. I kept arguing with her about what I could still wear. I would pull things out of the bags and put them on; some things would almost wrap around me twice. I knew I was losing weight and my clothes were baggy, but I had been so caught up in the emotional changes that I was not aware of the physical changes that were taking place. In the first year, I lost over 100 pounds. That weekend completely changed the way I saw myself.

I wanted to tell everyone about "gluten."

I told another friend that I ate "funny stuff" now. She gave me a strange look. I said, "I eat vegetables. I eat squash and zucchini. You know, funny stuff." The look on her face was priceless. She loved vegetables. Vegetables were foreign to me. In the past, I was closed off and refused to listen to anyone talking about anything healthy around me—that was for someone else. Now here I was describing how food had transformed my life. I stopped eating gluten and now I can talk. I can think. The fog has lifted. I have energy. I don't think about dying. I am excited to wake up each day. I no longer pretend to be grateful for the life I have. *I am grateful.*

24

In November, I decided to take my food plan to an even cleaner level. I knew there were other foods that were impacting my health. I did a 21-day cleanse (see Resources section). I did not eat any processed foods nor did I eat foods that are known to be allergens. While Carolyn and I both are highly gluten intolerant, and the responses we have after we eat it are quite similar, we have a very different relationship to food. I've always turned to food for comfort and to numb out. She went the opposite way, and would struggle to eat at all.

I knew I was still using sugar to numb my feelings. There was no way to prepare myself for the journey that cleanse would take me on. I eliminated sugar, processed foods, and caffeine from my diet. I did this process in stages, given I was not in a treatment center. For the first ten days, I wanted to crawl up the walls. If I had taken all processed and sugared foods out of my diet immediately, I don't think I would've lasted long enough to understand how those foods effect me.

11/24/2011 Gratitude: I'm not really sure what to title this. I'm having lots of thoughts related to food and emotions; to life and existing. I know as I go through this cleanse many different emotions have come up. I've said over and over that I had no idea about the emotional impact that doing this cleanse would have on me. No clue. As with many things I have done lately, I've known it is what I need to do.

I look back at last Thanksgiving, where I was really struggling. I had a psychotic break, according to my doctor; the first big one in years and it was hard to come back from it. I felt like I lost ground in my recovery at that time. I struggled with circling thoughts, paranoia, questioning everything around me—I fought to make it all stop.

A month before this episode happened, I had begun to work on my physical wellness by not drinking soda. This incident almost derailed that attempt. "Who cares if I get healthier? This is always going to be in my life," played over and over in my head like a broken record. Yet something pushed me through. I am no longer doing things because others want me to—that only worked for short periods of time.

I thought food was my comfort, the numbing agent to get me through life's horrible times. It became so much more than sustenance, so much more than fuel for my body, it became my armor—my protection. In fact, it was my nemesis and it was slowly killing me bite by bite. The food I was eating was stealing my health.

I still marvel that I was willing to try removing gluten from my diet. I remember when I felt that pop in my head—I felt a sense of freedom with my words I had never known or experienced. I was in awe. I didn't trust this for many weeks, then the undeniable proof—a few wrong foods eaten and I was a mess. Food. Once again it was robbing me of my mind. I'm so grateful that I know this. Today I am certain of the impact food has on my life–even though I struggle with the emotions I am currently feeling. No more lying to myself about food being protection.

I know today that I am in charge of my body and emotions. I am not a victim of this anymore. I am not saying that I will not experience pain, I am human. I'm saying that when I'm clean with my food, I'm clear about the emotions I'm feeling. No more plans for making it through the day or having to be prepared for certain times of the year by building in extra downtime. I no longer need those kinds of safeguards. I'm not the same.

I find that, for the first time in years, I haven't had any night terrors. I can't think of a time in my life that I've been this clear headed and feeling so raw emotionally–and I'm doing it–without comfort foods or medication. I used to tell myself that I was grateful to be alive. That statement was never really true. Something inside me always wondered if I would ever feel the peace everyone else talked about.

Even in the midst of the emotional turmoil that I've been experiencing while doing this cleanse, I feel peace. I know I can have a life where I know who will wake up in the morning. I know that I no longer have to fear going into a psychotic crisis. I know that the deep dark hole has been filled in. The freedom this has provided me cannot be measured. I had no way of knowing this was possible–absolutely no way, not a clue.

What if the pieces of this puzzle hadn't come together? I wouldn't have known this freedom. I know that not everyone is impacted so significantly with food, yet I imagine many people are and have no way of knowing it. I just KNOW many people out there are living a life which is significantly impacted by what they put in their mouths every day. They are, bite by bite, stealing life from themselves.

Life is short and precious. When you're told you're sick– you're ill, mentally ill–you have a brain disorder–you're crazy–and you're told you'll have this illness for the rest of your life, it alters how you see life and what's possible for you. So you take medication, which has its own negative impact on your body and mind, and try to learn to live with it all.

What if a large percentage of individuals really aren't mentally ill? What if they're food ill? I've been food ill, but labeled mentally ill. I say I've had reaction to trauma and food–period. Nothing more; nothing less. No organic defect.

I now live in this world with the knowledge that I am not less than others, that I'm not sick. I deserve to be here on this earth and breathe the air I breathe. I now am free to pursue life, fully and completely; open to whatever comes my way. Everything starts here with my food plan. If I don't manage what I eat, all those doors close. I *believe I'm here for a purpose, and I'm open to wherever life takes me. God, it feels good to say that and know it's true.*

Tomorrow is Thanksgiving—a day of thanks. I look forward to having a brand new experience of this day. So, Happy Thanksgiving to me! I'm grateful to be emerging out of my cocoon. It's been a long incubation and I'm ready to spread my wings and fly.

Not only did I remove all the foods I ate for comfort, but I did it during the holidays—the toughest season I experienced each year. I did it without any psychiatric medications. I had tough days, but they were tough because something *actually* happened, like the death of a friend, or that my house was robbed—*real stuff.* Everyday life simply worked itself out.

Slowly but surely, I was able to trust my new found way of living was real and wasn't going to disappear. I became accustomed to the new me. My co-workers were especially grateful, because I didn't chase them around to make sure they weren't upset with me. It was no longer necessary for me to spend all night recuperating from the day. I had energy left over. I was walking a couple of miles every morning before work, and sometimes rode my bike to work, too. I began to travel more while working on projects at the state level.

Friends and colleagues from Austin would often ask me about moving. My response had always been the same: I was committed to working at the hospital. While that was true, I was really too scared to make such a big change. I knew everyone at the hospital. I knew how they reacted to things. More importantly, they knew me and how I reacted to things. They knew what it took for me to get through the day. They were proud of me. The people I worked with thought I was inspiring and amazing because I had triumphed over my mental illness. I thought I needed the support and safety working at the hospital provided. I suddenly realized I was no different than anyone else. If I wanted to move to Austin, nothing was stopping me but me. The only requirement was that I stay on my food plan.

I did not need to be protected or have a safety net.

25

In February, 2012—one year after Carolyn and I talked that first time—I began telling people I was interested in moving. I heard about a job opening in an organization near Austin. The day I sat down to fill out the application, I could hardly breathe. It was the first job application I had ever filled out on my own. I kept telling myself,

"I can do this! I can do this!"

In less than six weeks, I got the job, packed up my house, moved, and traveled across the state facilitating trainings. A new town, a new job, a new life, and I felt better than ever. Little was familiar to me and it didn't matter. I went new places, called people I didn't know, and made appointments. Nothing was too difficult.

In May, however, I began thinking incessantly about my Mom. Life felt like a struggle again. I *knew* I had eaten something by accident. The reactions were clear. They followed the pattern of being glutened.

5/15/2012   This year I have experienced pure emotion for the first time in my life. After I recovered from last week's "gluten accident," I went through Mother's Day and the anniversary of Mom's death, and

was able to honor and celebrate my Mom. I went for a walk that day and was able to laugh when I got caught in the rain. I was fully present in the day, with moments of sadness because I miss her. I feel sad that she didn't get to know this Amy.

I'm experiencing a new sense of loss–loss associated with things that will never be in my life. It used to hurt to cry. I would do anything to avoid it. I cried last night. I cried hard, and it felt completely different. I cried about all the things I never got to do. I cried about all the experiences I didn't get to have. Then I stopped crying. Before now, I needed a medication "bomb" to stop crying. Not anymore. Nothing is the same.

The new issue I'm having is that I just want to go about my day–simple as that. It's surprising to me. I'm not having an emotional reaction to the fact that it is one of "those anniversaries." The people in my life, who know how I've dealt with these times of the year, are constantly calling to check on me. My friends and former co-workers phone calls, while thoughtful and loving, are reminding me of the past over and over again. The reminders of those anniversaries don't bother me as much as knowing how fragile people think I am–it's very frustrating.

I'm so angry right now, and almost don't know what to do. It's as though the anger is bubbling up and I just want to scream. I want to scream and run–I'm writing instead. I look at all the years I spent *living in so much emotional angst and turmoil, as well as the physical pain that came with it. It's like being in the Twilight Zone. One wrong bite and I'm back in the hole; five days later I pop out again.*

Unbelievable. Food. Food! I spent so many years in hell because of food. It wasn't some extended version of PTSD. It wasn't due to the extent of all the traumatic events I encountered. My psyche wasn't broken, nor was my ability to cope with life.

It was food!

26

As the one year anniversary of going fully gluten free approached, I was able to see myself from an entirely new point of view. I was able to look at the devastation, pain and anxiety that gluten caused in my life—without excessive or uncontrollable emotion. Instead, I felt a deep sense of gratitude.

6/25/2012 What a Difference a Year Makes...On July 1, 2011, I went fully gluten free. By then, life had already changed so much, simply because I stopped eating things I knew contained flour. My life hasn't been the same since that day. I had no idea where the path would lead when I embarked on this journey. Had I been told, I wouldn't have believed it. I didn't know the freedom eating a certain diet could provide. I'm deeply moved by all that happened in my life during this past year. The physical changes are a mere blip compared to the emotional changes I've experienced. I'm nothing like the woman who struggled to walk those laps at Tech Terrace one short year ago.

Today, I'm able to speak with ease at meetings, in front large audiences, and in personal conversations. The paralyzing anxiety is gone. There's an easy flow when I speak. I know the words I want to say will be there. I'm able to stand tall and walk confidently into a room. I'm learning to have fun and to enjoy life. I have energy. I feel like I'm just now learning how to live. Throughout this year I've taken risks. I've trusted myself and know I can handle whatever happens. What a beautiful thing!

For the first time in over 25 years, I have no psychiatric medications in my system. I stand in awe as I reflect over this past year. I have a whole new life. I will never be the same. I know what sends me into the black hole–it's gluten. If I accidentally eat gluten and slide back into the hole, all I have to do is wait 5 or 6 days, then a ladder comes down and I get to climb back up and out onto solid ground. It's amazing to me the life I'm able to lead, without fearing relapse into psychosis or deep depression. Such freedom! It's almost indescribable. It's taken a while for me to trust this freedom, but I do–implicitly.

The greatest gift I've received is the ability to release and bless events in my life that ruled the way I lived. In the past, I felt as though I did not belong on this earth, that I was not worthy of the breath I took. I begin this new year like an empty vessel, waiting to see what life has to offer. I wonder what gifts I'll receive. I look forward to getting to know myself as a person who is mentally well. I look forward to others coming to know me as a person who is mentally well. I'm ready to dream big.

It's so exciting to think about becoming who I am really meant to be. It's amazing how different it is to breathe. Everything seems very *different, very unknown, and new. I look forward to my body loosening up from the years I spent frozen. The ice has melted.*

In August of 2012, I went to Carolyn's doctor. I used to think going to the doctor was a burden. This time, I saw it as an opportunity to open doors that were still locked to me. I was optimistic and thought I was ready for anything. I was tested for food allergies, and had additional blood work done. I waited for the results with great anticipation.

I was learning how my body reacts to different foods, and knew I was still having reactions to something I was eating. When I received the results of my allergy test, I was speechless. The test confirmed my sensitivity to gluten and eggs. It also showed I had numerous other food sensitivities. I would've never thought to eliminate some of the foods on that list.

I walked out of the doctor's office with eyes as big as saucers. I kept thinking to myself, "Bring it on!" I gained freedom by removing gluten from my diet. If the price of freedom was to eliminate my favorite foods, then I would find new favorites. Most of the foods on my list don't effect me emotionally the way gluten and eggs do. However, I'm not willing to compromise any aspect of my life. I happily started living by the new food plan I was given, and began to feel *even better.*

I had one final anniversary to go through. On September 12, 2012, I celebrated, my first "Freedom Day." I made it one full year with no psychiatric medications, and had the best year of my life.

I found freedom. I am free.

Part Three

Carolyn

Writing our stories was daunting. It required us to break the unspoken rules we had about letting people know what was *really* going on with us, to let people see into our lives, and to dive deeply into what life was like for us. It was safer to keep the doors and windows shut. During this process we repeatedly had to face grief and loss. Approaching such a task while ill would have never been possible. We had to be strong enough to withstand the deep sadness that can accompany a review of the past. Mere glimpses of the past seemed crushing. Listening to the tape recordings of our conversations and reading our accumulated journals was a journey in and of itself.

By the time I was told to eat gluten free, I had nothing left. I had no idea how I was going to convince myself to live one more day. I had no plan for living, nor did I have a plan for dying. At the same time, Amy was convincing herself that she was grateful, even though she was barely hanging on. Neither one of us ever told anyone the real truth—it was getting harder and harder to make it through another day. We both refused to go to the doctor, go to the therapist, or take any more medication.

We had been through too much to ask for anymore "help."

2

Discovering the impact gluten had on our mental health saved our lives. The dreaded "deep, dark hole" of numbness and despair, we and others have described as mental illness, only exists for us with an accidental ingestion of gluten. To this day, if we eat something containing gluten, that wellness disappears within hours, and is gone for a minimum of five days until the symptoms subside.

Those symptoms are what we typically describe as psychological in nature: irritability, anxiety, paranoia, psychosis, and depression. All coping mechanisms from the past immediately and automatically return. At least now, we're able to recognize it for what it is—*know it will pass*—and that we'll be returned to wellness in short order. It happens each and every time we have an "accidental glutening."

Unfortunately, there is no way for us to estimate the hours we spent seeking treatment or the time we spent in some kind of treatment, nor can we estimate the hours provided to us from others (family, friends, and healthcare providers). It is also impossible to calculate the cost of it all—for just two people. The following pages outline the diagnoses, treatments, symptoms, and medications we were given throughout our lives, to the best of our recollection. When seen combined, the lists are staggering.

Emotional, Behavioral, and Physical Symptoms

Depression	Anxiety
Circular Thinking	Rapid Speech
Agitation	Helplessness
Self-Persecution	Panic Attacks
Hyper-Vigilance	Self -Imposed Isolation
Auditory Hallucinations	Hopelessness
Delusions	Overly Dramatic
Negative Self -Talk	Alcohol Abuse
Stuttering	Psychosis
Pacing	Reactive
Visual Hallucinations	Self -Abusive Behavior
Irritability	Excessive Talking
Emotional Outbursts	Frequent Crying
Night Terrors	Paranoia
Apologizing for Existing	Distorted Thoughts
Low Self-Esteem	Fear
Lost Time	Excessive Spending
Chronic Anemia	Diarrhea
Rashes	Cold Sweats
Chronic Yeast Infections	Restless Legs
Muscle Cramps	Swollen Joints
Elevated Liver Enzymes	Dry Skin

Itching Ears/Nose

Chronic Constipation

Shaking

Chewing on Lips

Dry Mouth

Twirling Fingers

Excessive Sleeping

Itchy, Dry Scalp

Floaters and Spots in Eyes

Mouth Sores

Hair Loss

Suicidal Thoughts/Plans/Attempts

Difficulty Formulating Sentences

Uncontrollable Sobbing

Cold Hands and Feet

Itching Throat

Exhaustion

Itchy Skin

Weak and Ridged Nails

Stomach Aches

Red, Swollen Gums

Night Sweats

Ear Aches

Migraines

Sugar Cravings

Slow Blinking

Eye Twitching

Flashes of Anger

Diagnoses

Agoraphobia

Attention Deficit Disorder

Morbid Obesity Disorder

Chronic Ear Infections

Seasonal Allergies

Pregnancy Arthritis

General Anxiety Disorder

Eczema

Clinical Depression

Irritable Bowel Syndrome

Schizoaffective Disorder

Anorexia/Bulimia

Ophthalmic Migraine

Chronic Bronchitis

Social Anxiety Disorder

Hysterical Paralysis

Psychosomatic Disorder

Hypoglycemia

Dysthymia

Major Depressive Disorder

Borderline Personality Disorder

Post Traumatic Stress Disorder

Seasonal Affective Disorder

Bipolar Disorder

Hypochondria

Asthmatic

Restless Leg Syndrome

Pre-Diabetes

TMJ

Dysthymia

Major Depression with Psychotic Tendencies

Treatments, Therapies, and Groups

Individual Psychotherapy

Assertive Community Treatment

Eating Disorder Treatment

Cognitive Behavioral Therapy

Experiential Therapies

Hydro Colon Therapy

Psychiatric Out-Patient Treatment

Chiropractic Treatment

Electro-Convulsive Therapy

SCIO Quantum Biofeedback

Psychiatric In-Patient Treatment

Alcoholics Anonymous

Alcohol/ Drug Treatment

Hypnosis

Psychopharmacology

Clergy Sessions

Massage Therapy

Group Psychotherapy

Tomatis Audio Therapy

Prayer Groups

Nutritional Therapy

Laser/Light Therapy

Church Retreats

Al-Anon

Dual Recovery Anonymous

Emotions Anonymous

Over Eaters Anonymous

Narcotics Anonymous

Medications

Abilify	Adderall	Albuterol
Ambien	Benadryl	Buspar
Celebrex	Celexa	Cogentin
Depakote	Effexor	Elavil
Geodon	Guaifed	Imodium
Klonopin	Lamictal	Lexapro
Lithium	Lorazepam	Mellaril
Neurontin	Paxil	Pepto Bismol
Prednisone	Prevacid	Provigil
Prozac	Risperdal	Ritalin
Sarafem	Seroquel	Stelazine
Tegretol	Thorazine	Tofranil
Topamax	Tramadol	Trazodone
Trilafon	Valium	Wellbutrin
Xanax	Zoloft	Zyprexa

Multiple Anti-Inflammatory Medications and Antibiotics

These lists are not complete.

3

Amy and I have learned a lifetime's worth of lessons in the past several years. Our entire perception of living has changed. Many of our experiences have been exciting and charged with possibility. Many experiences have been extremely difficult. I had no way of estimating what it would be like to suddenly be "awakened" as I was pushing hard on 50 years old. I looked great and I felt great. I was experiencing a life that I had given up on so very long ago. I became comfortable in my own skin for the first time. I grew accustomed to my new-found "lack of reaction to the world." Over a short period of time, I began to understand the dietary cleaning up we did simply allowed us to function in a basic way.

For me, the diet change couldn't undo a lifetime of lost work, a resume full of unexplainable holes, and completely ruined credit. Amy's lack of formal education has prevented her from being able to be promoted. The wreckage of a life lived as a diagnosed and seemingly broken person remained.

Amy and I have often discussed the societal and developmental markers we missed. Movies, books, music and world events alter and shape an individual's adult development. Being heavily medicated and hidden away from "regular" life creates many gaps in a person's knowledge and acquired experience. It is uncommon to think about how much we actually learn about living on a daily basis.

In general, we don't often think about the unspoken expectations we have of ourselves and others to accomplish certain things by a certain age—especially regarding work and financial stability. Knowing things like how to tell when the yard is dying, tricks to laundry and cooking, what's a good investment, and how to manage a 401K are bits of information we simply absorb or learn along the way. There may be a connection between these experiential learning gaps and the high suicide rate of the older "mentally ill" population. I am constantly surprised by the things I know I *should* know—yet don't. Though I work at it diligently, I cannot begin to fill in those gaps. I am certain there are many others out there—just like us.

While we were writing, a dear friend's brother took his life after a life-long struggle with mental illness. He was 69 years old. On that day, this book became the message it was meant to be in the first place—a message of hope regarding alternative solutions for mental health.

4

Being able to share my experience with Amy was one of the greatest gifts of my life. I knew I couldn't be the only person on this planet of seven billion people to suffer with emotional, paranoid, and sometimes psychotic symptoms as a result of food intolerances and allergies. I was blessed with guiding Amy through her first year of gluten-free eating. It was an honor to be allowed into her life at such a deep and profound level.

There are not enough ways for us to say we're thankful to no longer live in the experience of confusion and heartbreak that previously constituted our lives. We're now free to interact with others, free to choose to participate in activities or not, and free to say yes to invitations without worrying about our "limited abilities."

It is a gift that our bodies are meant to heal themselves. Over these past several years, our bodies have become stronger and healthier than ever before. It is amazing what can happen when one stops ingesting things the body cannot handle. As we have both said, most of our physical and emotional symptoms have systematically disappeared. It truly is a testament to the resiliency and spirit embodied in the human being.

Our loved ones no longer feel a need to pray that we be released from despair. Now their prayers are for giving thanks. It's wonderful to have people cheering you on. Today, we are truly grateful to be alive and well. We are grateful to be able to share our experiences of a miraculous healing. We have been able to share this knowledge with others, and have had the privilege of watching them heal. What a remarkable gift this has become.

We are not saying this is the only answer for wellness. However, it was the answer for us. For the first time in our lives, we can count on ourselves completely. We *know with absolute certainty* who is going to wake up every day. On days when we have had an accident, we know it will be over soon.

That certainty is our "greatest miracle."

Many times, we have been asked, "Where is the statistical evidence?" I am evidence. Amy is evidence. That is all I need, all Amy needs, all our families, friends, and co-workers need. We invite you to find your own evidence or, better yet, *become* your own evidence.

We travel and speak about the devastating impact food has had on our lives and our triumphant return to wellness. We share our stories as a way to teach and inspire others toward a life of wellness. We want people to know there may be a surprising cause for mental illness. It's a different place to look and its right under your nose. What you put in your mouth might have everything to do with your wellness—or your illness. You are the one who gets to choose what goes in your mouth.   Mental illness to wellness can be that simple.

For us, mental wellness begins with food.

Afterword

Gluten intolerance is a growing problem of the modern world, much like diabetes, cancer and obesity. These conditions have always existed, but were so uncommon that nobody studied them or understood their origins. Today, almost one third of the population is reacting to gluten. This is not common knowledge because the increase in people's reaction to gluten is new. Additionally, gluten sensitivity produces health conditions that are thought to be independent conditions with their own labels or diagnoses.

Gluten stirs up the immune system, which can cause inflammation and damage to ANY tissue. The immune system is what constantly regulates, repairs, and maintains every tissue. Problems found within the immune system are critical, varied, and can be widespread. These problems cause obvious symptoms for some, and subtle, diffuse collections of symptoms for others. Until very recently, no one knew that bipolar disorder, multiple sclerosis, Lou Gehrig's disease, autoimmune diseases of the joints, skin, pancreas, liver, brain, and more could be caused by gluten.

Millions of people around the world present with mental symptoms, are quickly diagnosed, and are treated as having psychiatric illnesses. Physical illness is not even considered. Many people are still seriously sick from gluten, and have no doctors to help them. This is a low point in modern medicine. We the public must stand up for ourselves, and demand the physical cause of mental symptoms be thoroughly examined.

This book describes two people and their lifelong experiences with gluten, and other foods, having caused inflammation in the brain—a *physical* organ with a *physical* illness. These two courageous women began their journeys when no one knew to look at the impact food could have on the body and mind. I am grateful they are sharing their stories. Understanding what is hiding in the shadows offers me the ability to show my patients new possibilities for health.

Dr. Will Mitchell, LAc, DOM (NM), MS Nutrition
Merritt Wellness Center
Austin, TX

Resources

"Celiac Disease: A Hidden Epidemic"

by Peter H. R. Green, M.D. and Rory Jones

www.celiacdiseasecenter.org

"Cleanse: Detox Your Body, Mind and Spirit"

by Betty Murray, CN, HHC, RYT

www.cleansethebook.com

"Wheat Belly"

by Dr. William Davis

www.wheatbelly.com

"The UltraMind Solution"

by Mark Hyman, M.D.

www.drhyman.com

drhyman.com/blog/2011/03/17/gluten-what-you-dont-know-might-kill-you/#

"Psychology Today"

www.psychologytoday.com

www.psychologytoday.com/blog/evolutionary-psychiatry/201108/wheat-and-serious-mental-illness

"The G-Free Diet: A Gluten Free Survival Guide"

by Elizabeth Hasselbeck

Our Health Providers

Shades of Hope Treatment Center   www.ShadesofHope.com

Restoration Health   www.RestorationHealth.net

The Hills Medical Group   www.CenterforHealthandHealing.org

Merritt Wellness   www.MerrittWellness.com

Frankl Clinic   www.FranklClinic.com

A Special Thanks

To Og Mandino, whose book, "The Greatest Miracle in the World,"
kept us bound together through many years.

Acknowledgments

We are deeply appreciative of the love and support we have received throughout our lives. We are especially thankful for:

Our Mothers, Judy and Gayle: who never stopped loving us, hoping for us, searching for us, praying for us.

Our Fathers, Denny and Gordon: whose love runs deep and wide.

Our Grandmothers: who loved us dearly and taught us more than they could have imagined.

Our Grandfathers: who adored us simply because we exist.

Our Brothers, Mike and Jeremy: because we love you.

Alex, my purest gift from God: thank you for the beautiful spirit you are, the blessing you are, the teacher you are, the joy you are—it is my ultimate privilege to be your mom.

Kathy: thank you for championing me and loving me as your own.

Our longtime friends, Deborah and Angela: thank you for being people who are bigger than judgment and reason, whom we love deeply.

The people who have housed us at various points along the way: we are deeply grateful for your generosity.

Those who walked with us, talked with us and listened to us for hours on end as we became well: especially Anita Correnti, Chad McFadon, Eileen Dyer, Mike Rinehart, and Ronda Nelson.

All who assisted in reading and editing: Chad McFadon, Deborah Milosevich, Eileen Dyer, Janet Zaretsky, Michael Ventura, Robyn Priest, Tania Vona, Vickie Barnes and *especially* Christina Proper.

About the Authors

Carolyn Marsalis holds a Master's Degree in Education, Counseling, and Human Development, is a Certified Holistic Health and Life Coach, a PeerZone USA Facilitator, a SoulCollage® Facilitator and is an Instructor at The Institute of Transformational and Transpersonal Coaching. She has developed a coaching program which is focused on regaining mental health and recovering from the effects of post traumatic stress. Carolyn served as Treasurer on the Texas Catalyst for Empowerment Board of Directors.

Amy Pierce is the owner of Resiliency Unleashed Training & Consulting. She is a Certified Peer Specialist, a PeerZone USA Coordinator, an Advanced Level WRAP Facilitator, a WHAM Facilitator, and an ASIST Trainer. She began the first Peer Support Program in the Texas State Hospital System. Amy served as Chair on the Protection and Advocacy for Individuals with Mental Illness (PAIMI) Advisory Council and the Texas Catalyst for Empowerment Board of Directors. Additionally she served as Treasurer on the Board of Directors for Disability Rights Texas.

Carolyn and Amy speak internationally
regarding the effects of food on mental health.

To schedule a speaking engagement, visit www.FoodandMentalHealth.com

Made in the USA
Middletown, DE
09 September 2020